CU01023123

My Shamba in Kenya
by
"Surengu"

Being an account of work and incidents on

Kenya farms from 1947 to 1962, when advice on

tropical agriculture was minimal and experiments

showed the way.

ISBN 0 9529653 0 5
978

Published by Fireside Press.
Sleights, Whitby. 3 YO22 5DJ

CONTENTS

To
My wife Mavis for her patience and love for the man who was dedicated to the soil and livestock.

Introduction

It was shortly after being demobbed from the Air Force that my brother-in-law decided that he was fed up with a mixed farm and would like to try his hand at farming in Australia if I would join him. I had no hesitation and we got a lot of literature about Australia, and whilst in London called at the Colonial Office on the prospects of farming in Kenya. After studying the pros and cons of each destination we thought the prospects of Kenya were worth a visit, and if we were disappointed we would go on to Australia.

Travel by air in 1948 was slow and unreliable, and after a hold-up in Khartoum we arrived at Kisumu on Lake Victoria. There was no international airport at Nairobi or at Entebbe in Uganda in those days. We must have just missed the twice weekly rail journey to Nairobi as we were told to wait three days for the twelve hour journey, but our luck was in by the fact that a small plane could get to Nairobi at once.

The next day we got a second-hand car and set off to tour the country, firstly around Nairobi and Kiambu and part of the Aberdares. Then we stayed a few days in Nakuru looking at farms in the Rift Valley and then a few days in Lumbwa looking at that area, and then on to Eldoret and the land on the Uasin Gishu plateau. Finally we ended up in Kitale in the Trans Nzoia district.

We saw farms from three thousand to ten thousand feet above sea level, and sizes from a few hundred to ten thousand acres, and fertility ranging from deep volcanic loam to hardly any soil at all, and crops that differed from coffee to sisal and maize to pyrethrum, and at the best time of the year to observe them.

Apart from the wide ranging crops, soils and altitude there was another factor which was so obvious that it stood out a mile. It was the management. Very few farms were well managed and the results were clearly to be seen.

During the next twelve months I helped build a house and homestead and cleared most of the land of scrub, and then worked as a manager on some large farms, and for the last few years I farmed on my own account.

Farming in the Trans Nzoia, Kenya

The district of Trans Nzoia lies in the north west of Kenya bordered on the north by the native locations of the Suk and Karamajong tribes, to the east by the district of Uasin Gishu and the Nzoia River, to the south by the native location of Kakemega of and to the west by Mount Elgon and Uganda. That was about 3500 square miles.

It lies one degree north of the Equator at the altitude of 6000 -6600 feet above sea level and the soil varies from abrasive red to a kind of gravel known as murram, heavy black soil of areas subject to flooding, and very fertile volcanic soil around Mount Elgon. It is undulating country interspaced by many streams and three rivers the Nzoia, Noigamaget and Moiben. Very little land is too steep to be cultivated. It was covered in scrub trees of various kinds about twelve feet tall, others of flat topped acacia thorn and bigger useful trees near streams and rivers, and giant Podocarpus near Mount Elgon.

The rainfall is about 60 inches from the south west and north east monsoons. It is very predictable in that the first rains from the south west monsoon would start around 9th of March and continue through April and May. June was usually drier. The heavy rains were usually in July and August and some showers in November and again around Christmas and the New Year, often accompanied by hailstones which were as big as marbles and able to devastate a crop. We recorded the daily rainfall and the heaviest downfall was four inches in 20 minutes, 20 minutes fine, then three and a half inches in 20 minutes, i.e. seven and a half inches in one hour.

Needless to say damage was severe, dams that had been constructed 30 years before were washed away also many roads and bridges.

There was a low lying area of about 20,000 acres which was the home of the deer called tope, and this was flooded by about five feet of water and the few thousand deer evacuated to neighbouring farms causing more damage. I think the year was 1960 and the Owen Falls dam at the outfall of the Victoria Nyanza could not cope with this volume of water and the lake level was raised three feet in a matter of a month when it was intended to raise to that level over ten years.

The area was largely uninhabited except for a very few nomadic tribes. The remains of their small encampments could be

2

found here and there. The reason was that it was teeming with game including a lot of lion and elephant. I think it was first discovered by the Europeans about 1890 and prior to that it had been crossed by Arab slave traders bringing slaves from Uganda on a trail at the foot of Mount Elgon, which stands at 13,000 feet and is sometimes snow capped.

I heard from one soldier settler from the First World War that he had once shot seven lions in one day before Sunday lunch. There was a range of hills called Cherangani about fifty miles south of Mount Elgon and the soldier settler said that herds of elephant used to pass the area annually before it was settled and fences erected.

Clearing the Land

Clearing of the scrub was done by hand using the double-headed axe called a mattock, and on average it took eight men a day to clear an acre. One dense patch that I cleared took 25 man days but that was unusual. I insisted that no soil was to be returned to holes where the stump had been removed to a depth of nine inches, to avoid breakage later by the plough. If you didn't, the African would chop it off at ground level and cover the stump with soil. The scrub was then dragged off by teams of oxen to an area near to the brick maker for burning the hand-made bricks, the tile kiln, and to the labour lines for their fuel.

If the area had only a slight fall it was advisable to terrace it to prevent soil erosion. I have seen hundreds of acres rendered virtually useless by having all the top soil washed into the river bed with gulleys several feet deep.

To ensure that this did not happen, and to preserve the fertility of the land for future generations, all the land that had a slope was terraced to avoid erosion, but land that had a slope of one in eight was regarded as too steep for cultivation. The Agriculture Dept. encouraged this to be done and would advise on a scheme, and would supply surveyors and also strongly recommended that all crops be drilled or planted on the contour.

The first thing to be done when the land had been cleared of scrub was to select any depressions in the area to use as spillways from the terraces, and these were not ploughed. These would be about ten yards wide. As it was deemed that the terrace should empty into a spillway of not more than three hundred yards length, these spillways could be six hundred yards apart with the terraces flowing both ways. A shorter distance was advisable if a depression could be found.

SOIL CONSERVATION

Broad based terrace on 10% slope

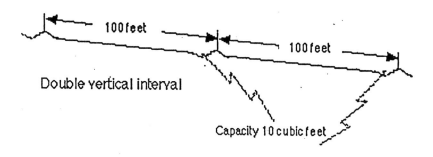

Normal vertical interval

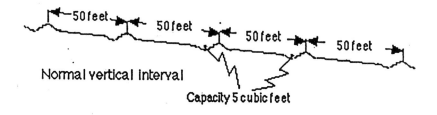

Fall in the terrace 1 in 100 on each type.
Maximum run to spillway 200 yards

    A surveyor with a theodolite would then mark out these terraces on the contours with a fall of one in a hundred into the spillways, and the interval between each terrace was ten vertical feet, thereby the terraces would not be parallel as they would be wider on areas that did not have much slope.
    The broad base terrace was favoured as all the land would

be cropped, instead of a deep cut that could not be cultivated and would harbour couch grass that spread very quickly.

The construction of these terraces would be done when the soil was moist and thereby compacted, by ploughing along these contours with the plough throwing up to the pegs and forming a rig, and ploughing about four yards each side. This would be repeated by ploughing three yards either side, then two yards either side, which gave sufficient loose soil to be shaped by a grader on the upper side. Only a few passes with the grader would construct the terrace to be about two feet six inches deep and about ten feet wide, giving a cross section of about 10 sq. feet, thus a capacity of about 10 cubic feet per foot run.

The maintenance of the terraces to keep their capacity was somewhat difficult. If the ploughing wasn't closely supervised the ox drivers would plough the easy way whereby the dead furrow would be central between each pair of terraces thereby losing fertility. There were several ways of ploughing these terraces by setting ridges in various places and still maintaining their capacity, but sometimes they had to be graded again. Most of this work was done in the slack time of July and August.

If the reversible plough had been invented in those days the maintenance of these terraces would have been 'a piece of cake'.

There was one character who was very keen on soil conservation, to the extent that many farmers believed that if he could have found a way of terracing a billiard table he would have done it!

Throughout the district there were many anthills, on average about two per acre. The most I have known was seven. They were of the broad based type varying from two to six feet high, unlike the ones in Uganda which were of the pedestal type. Sometimes the crown would have to be dug off to enable the ox ploughs to get over them, and continually ploughing leaving the dead furrow in the centre until they were eliminated. Some farmers used a bulldozer but when costed this proved rather too expensive.

A disc plough was used both for ox and tractor ploughing. The four furrow tractor plough was only used in emergencies, it was rather expensive. The ox ploughs were two furrow with 28" discs of three makes; Ransome Statesman, Cockshut, and one other (I forget its name). The last two were fairly light and worked well, in moist easy soil, but were of little use to make a good job on hard dry land mainly due to the limited adjustments that could be made, whereas the Ransome could be adjusted in both lateral and vertical ways, also furrow width, cross beam, point draw, height of hake and furrow wheel. When one considers that the plough had to hug the furrow wall when throwing uphill without crabbing, and also take a full furrow when throwing downhill without the weight of the tractor to hold it, the setting had to be accurate. Some of the ploughs had a long beam that would take three furrows, but to plough two 9-10" furrows 9" deep was enough work for a team of 16 oxen.

Opening up was usually done by one good ox driver who could plough an opening furrow as straight as any tractor driver. The rate of work was one and a half acres per ox team per seven hour day, and around an acre a day on terraced land that had many short ends.

The work oxen were of the native type with a hump, of boran or native cross. The former were rather bigger. To maintain the oxen work force of about 400, there were 400 cows producing some 300 calves which were earmarked at six month intervals also on the year. When the oxen were five years old they were replaced by one and a half year olds up to a total of 22 per team that were matched for colour. The reason for 22 for a 16 team was that some could be injured or sick and trainee oxen shouldn't be worked more than every other day to start with, and the last thing one had to avoid was that a driver should have to borrow one from another team to make it up. The drivers took pride in their teams.

The two leading oxen were given names and when turning left or right that particular ox was called to make the turn in that direction. Four of the biggest oxen were placed to the rear of the team and known as "wheelers" because they kept the plough going straight when turning. Our headlands were made about 10 yards wide, about half the team would be turning when the plough emerged from the furrow. As the fields were of one hundred to one hundred and fifty acres in size, two ploughs would be allocated to each 'rig', but if there were a lot of arguments as to who was ploughing badly (it couldn't be proved), this was abandoned and only one was used. Thereby the ploughman or driver could be rewarded or disciplined as the case may be.

The harness of an ox team comprised a yoke, a round piece of hardwood about 4'' diameter and 5 feet long, a half inch U bolt in the centre and two slots 1" by 3" at each end and about a foot between them. Down these two slots went two skeys. These were home made from hardwood 18" long and 3" by 1". On one side of each, there were two or three notches cut, and and the top was thicker so it would drop through the slot. A rawhide strop of hide about 3' 6" long adjoined end to end that had been twisted until about 15" long and had a loop at each end that fitted into the slots on the skey under the neck of the oxen, and could be adjusted accordingly on the notches.

A rawhide short trench was tied to the U bolt on the yoke and to the trek chain that was 8' long. A rein was tied around the horns of the ox to the U bolt on the yoke to prevent it escaping should the strop become loose. The trek chains were then coupled to each other by the hook and ring at each end. They could be coupled on to the U bolt but this was considered inadvisable in that some accident may occur whereby that particular yoke could be cut free.

TREK OXEN HARNESS

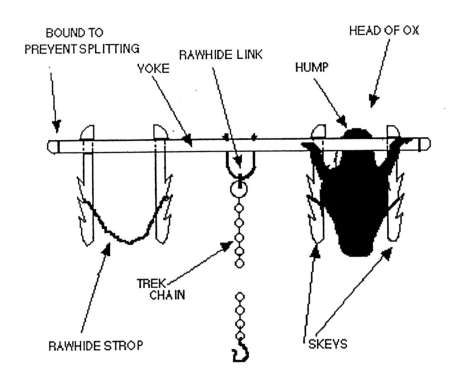

The reins and strops were made on the farm from hides of fallen stock, or from hides from animals slaughtered for meat for the labour. These had been sun dried on a frame sprinkled with salt. Four hides were soaked for a day or so until supple, and then cut in strips round and round the hide in one piece about one and a half inches wide.

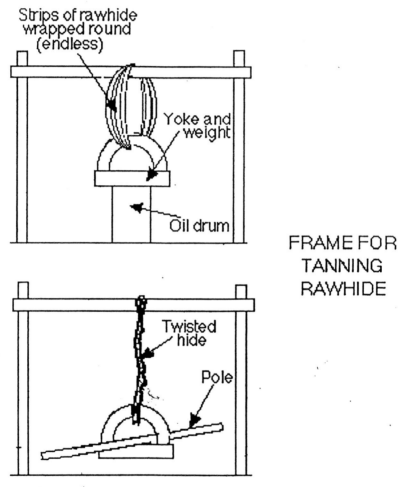

FRAME FOR
TANNING
RAWHIDE

Then four strips were attached to the ends of each and wound around a tree branch about ten feet off the ground, and through a yoke of wood and a weight of about one and a half cwts. onto an empty oil drum. The two ends were then tied and the oil drum removed.

A pole about 10' long was pushed through the yoke and the

hides were twisted round and round until tight. Then the pole was removed and allowed the twisted hide to unwind and be wound the other way, with the pole inserted into the yoke and wound again to the top. This would be done for about two days, when the hide would be pliable, fairly dry and white in colour. Any breakage would have been pieced together as and when it occurred.

The hide was then given a liberal amount of vegetable oil and twisted for a further four days and given more oil as required to make soft and supple rawhide reins.

The whips the drivers used were best made from giraffe hide that could be obtained from the Game Dept. from animals that had been culled or injured on the roads. The whips were about twelve feet long and attached to a staff about eight feet long. The end was tied to the staff about half way up. Thus it was a closed whip. It was found that too many oxen were blinded by using an open whip and this policy was rigorously enforced.

The Labour Force

The labour force I used was split evenly between the three tribes whose locations were near the Trans Nzoia, namely the Jalua, Bugishu, and Kitosh, and the reason for this was that tribal customs were very strong, and if I had any trouble, I could not be held to ransom, as in no way would all three gang up together. I could always carry on reasonably well with a two thirds labour force until new labour arrived. I suppose it was the age old system of divide and rule.

All were housed either in brick houses or native style huts, and were given two pounds of maize meal per day plus an issue of vegetables in season, salt, bananas and one pound of sugar (if not absent without reason) each week, and an ox would be slaughtered most weeks. I would have liked it to have been a free issue, but no matter how it was given there would be complaints as to some getting meat without bone and others getting offal. So it was decided one reliable African should pay five cents per lb (two and a half new pence) and sell it at about the same price, and the head was for his trouble. If by any chance he was not doing it fairly the labour would complain and he was relieved of his job, and it was given to another (there were many waiting in the wings to do it). It worked well and very few changes were made to the purveyor.

All married men were given half an acre vegetable plot, and a few reliable or experienced married men who were engaged on contract for a year at a wage rather less than the others, were given

9

two acres, but were obliged to turn out their family for work when required.

The working day was from 7 a.m. until 2 p.m. six days per week with no break for refreshments for a wage of 30 East African shillings per month each, the equivalent of an English shilling, for ordinary labourers and somewhat less for juveniles. This remuneration seems a pittance but in the 1950s it was double the remuneration in the African Locations and that didn't include rations or housing.

About 1960 the Labour Dept. decided that a minimum wage plus rations for a 48 hour week of about 35 shillings was to be enforced. I discussed it with the labour and as they didn't want to work Saturday afternoons the daily hours would have to be increased, and as an extra hour and a half would have to be worked each day without refreshments it was decided to break at 11 a.m. to 1 p.m. to have a meal. The system worked for three days when they decided they wanted to go back to the previous system.

I told them that it wasn't allowed as it was a Government directive, but they said it had been devised by some idiot in the government who had never done a day's manual work in his life, and that particular person had better come and demonstrate how to do it. They reverted to the old system and nothing more became of it. The system of working eight hours non-stop would not have worked with teams of oxen but a break at mid-day for 2 or 3 hours would have worked well.

A lot of work was done by piece work but as this required more supervision one had to select a very good foreman to oversee the work.

The rates of pay for supervisors and craftsmen are listed below.

Senior Headman	350 sh.	Blacksmith	250
Storeman	200	Carpenter	250
Clerk	200	Bricklayer	200
Head ox-driver	250	Head herdsman (cattle)	250
Tractor driver	120	Foreman	80-120
	Ox drivers	80-100	

These figures may seem rather high compared with the labourers' wage of 30 sh. but as I couldn't be everywhere to supervise, I demanded a high standard of loyalty and paid them accordingly. They were conscious of the fact they could easily be reduced to the ranks and replaced by any labourer who showed an aptitude for the work.

My supply of labour was one of my lesser problems. Some farmers had some difficulty in maintaining their labour force and often the reason could not be clearly defined. Housing could be good, wages about the same, rations were right and work rate fairly good, but there could be others such as trouble makers, or even a witch doctor they had unconsciously employed, but more of them later.

Some farmers resorted to having a person recruiting in the native locations, but I tried it once and found there was a racket, in that the labour recruited would leave after the first month when the recruiter had got his bonus. I felt sure there was collusion between the recruiter and the recruited whereby the recruiter could get a good wage for months on end by virtually doing nothing.

Various misdemeanours and thefts were I think fairly well handled. Offences at work were often punished by loss of a day's pay, usually recommended by the foreman. Loss or theft of tools caused a cut in pay of double the value of the item. I found that just the value of the item encouraged them because I could buy them cheaper than they could and I was virtually a good shop.

Other offences which had nothing to do with the farm, such as stealing from each other, fighting, rape and others, were handled by a Court of Elders from each of the main tribes. None of the Elders were foremen or otherwise in authority. This Court often deliberated at length, maybe a full day on a case, and they would report to me on their verdict, which often seemed too severe for the offence. More often than not I queried the sentence, and usually they would not reduce it.

The culprit was then asked if he accepted the punishment and if he refused he had the option of being tried in a Magistrates Court. Just a few opted for this Court and usually the sentence was doubled, in that the Magistrates didn't want their Courts cluttered up with offences that had been fairly well handled by the Court of Elders.

In the late 1940s and early 50s the kiboko or whip was the punishment for certain offences until repealed in the late 50s. When this punishment was decided by the Court of Elders and they were

11

adamant it should be carried out, there was the question of who should do it. If it was done by a member of his own tribe it would be farcical, on the other hand if done by another tribesman it would be sadistic. I therefore administered the punishments myself. It was done in the presence of the leader of the Elders out of view of would-be spectators.

An Askari (farm policeman) was posted in the vicinity with instructions to apprehend any would-be spectators.

Their acceptance of this form of punishment was remarkable as I was usually shaken by the hand with a thank-you, and the matter was then closed, but should any of them harbour a grievance against the offender he would be liable to be summoned to the Court of Elders and probably given the same treatment.

Any fines that were made were put into an account for the benefit of the farm labourers, such as footballs and their kit, but this did not include boots as they played barefoot. Other items such as things for the farm school were also bought but always with the approval of the Senior Headman or school teacher.

There was one thing I learned very early in my dealings with the African, was to be fair and very firm. If there was any doubt whatsoever with any alleged offence it was advisable to dismiss it, but on the other hand, to let them get away with an offence would very soon lead to insubordination. Maybe my six years with the Provost Corps during the war helped a lot in my control of them.

The tribes of Africans vary quite a lot, but there are two main types. The Nilotic, such as the Masai, Suk, Karamajong who are generally pastoral. They are tall with fine features and may be described as haughty in that they regard the other main types the Bantu as inferior to them. Their dress was minimal, just a sheet tied over one shoulder, and usually plenty of heavy ear-rings which made the lobes so stretched that they would loop over the ear. Their hair was matted with sheep fat, maybe with some decoration, and on festive occasions adorned with ostrich feathers. As they had no pockets, a recess was made in the matted hair at the nape of the neck, in which to keep any coins they may have.

Primarily we recruited them as cattle herdsmen, guards for crops and milkers. They regarded work with a hoe or other cultivation as beneath them. I remember one incident when one of these tribesmen was given a herd of 500 steers to supervise, and after about a week he reported one morning. As he couldn't count I counted for him and found one to be missing. He described the missing steer in detail, and as there were no vultures hovering over the area where they were grazing I presumed it must have been stolen. But I had my doubts as cattle were never stolen as odd ones. Then three or four days later vultures were hovering over a spot and on closer examination we found the steer down an ant-bear hole and on pulling it out found it to be exactly as he had described.

The other type, the Bantu, were shorter, fatter, with Negroid features and dressed more or less conventionally. They cut their hair and had very few ear-rings, but most had two teeth extracted from the front of the lower jaw. The custom I believe was so that they could be fed if they got lockjaw. They were very versatile and could be trained as ox drivers, tractor drivers, brick and tile makers, and even blacksmiths, mechanics and bricklayers.

They were a happy crowd, often singing and story telling and I often teased them over my blue eyes, since never before had most of them seen blue eyes, and I told them they were special in that they could see around corners, and if I concentrated could even see through the walls of their houses what they were up to with their wives and girl friends.

As far as religion goes, only a few would go to the Missions that were here and there. I think the majority of these would go to the Roman Catholic one. The Suk tribes seemed to have a religion or custom that took place on Saturdays. They would assemble in a circle and the one in the middle would jump high in the air until tired and was replaced by another one. This continued for hours, I suppose until they they were all tired.

Circumcision was carried out by all tribes, but only on boys. I think the Kikuyu tribe still carry it out on girls. It was done on the farm by an 'expert' and at a ceremony. A group of boys aged about twelve or thirteen were done at a time, they were made to stand in the river for some part of the night and were circumcised at dawn.

Their bodies were smeared with a kind of white paint. It looked like ashes mixed with water, and they discarded their trousers and wore shouks (a cloth tied over one shoulder) for a few months and also kept their paint on. No one who had escaped the circumcision ceremony was allowed to take a wife, but that did not strip them of their ego I can assure you.

Other customs seem rather strange to us, such as not to pat a small child on the head. Their belief is that it will stop the child from growing big and strong. Another is that of the Suk tribes, whose ultimate greeting is to spit on one's face. We consider it to be the complete opposite of the best of greetings, but when one considers that our affectionate greeting is a kiss on the mouth, is this more hygienic?

The witch doctor (Macherwi) was still there despite the legislation by Government to stop it. They cannot since it has been carried out since the year dot. The African is very reluctant to identify one, and if he does it will only be done in a whisper in passing. No one must know he has divulged his existence, which made identification difficult, but one had to get rid of them.

When cats' paws, hens feet, chicken bones and other symbols were appearing on doorsteps, I found the best way was to try to find the area suspected of housing one, and with the help of the police, make a search of all the houses to find the tricks of the trade.

It is a fact that if a death spell is cast on a person he will die if he can't get the services of the Muganga to relieve the spell. I think that these two, (the one that casts the spell and the one that relieves it) must work together.

One day I had a tip off and caught one red-handed as soon as he got on the farm. The farm policeman was scared stiff of him, so I relieved him of the tricks of his trade, locked him in the storeroom and called the police.

There must have been a dozen different items all wrapped in individual cloths. There were hens' feet, rabbit paws, cats' paws, bones, snake skins, stones, shells and other things which the police took away along with the witch doctor.

I never heard what happened to him.

Crops

After many attempts to improve fertility and soil conditions by the use of green manure (mainly sunflower) I settled on a rotation of seven years in units of 400-450 acres. It was maize followed by either wheat, oats, barley, or sunflower, ending with maize undersown with grass.

This was about 3000 acres of the 4000 under rotation, and the 1000 acres was rough grazing, labourers' gardens, roads, dams, and river beds.

Maize

The maize that I grew was the white variety, and was a mixture of three different types and characteristics. One variety was

Natal Horsetooth. It was a large cob that was short in the sheaf of husk, that left some of the grains exposed and damaged by the weather. It was mainly 14 and 16 rows. It had great depth of seed, was rather soft, and would shed badly when thrown into a heap when harvesting. It was a heavy yielder but required a lot of rain and was rather poor in quality.

Another was Hickory King, that was an 8 row with a small core, rather flinty, very well sheathed, very good quality but not a high yielder.

The other was Pochestroom Parl which was drought resistant, 12 rows, very flinty, well sheathed, rather short round grains that did not shed very easily when harvested.

There was another variety that was multicoloured. It was a good yielder, well sheathed, a good flinty grain, but had one serious fault. The grain was very loose to the extent that it could be stripped from the cob by just twisting it between two hands. By our method of harvesting and throwing it into heaps, most of the grain would shed. It was known as Mdoor-door, this maybe a Swahili word as 'm' is often used at the beginning of a word. But as maize was introduced from South America in about the 16th century, and is is identical with that still grown in the Andes, could this word have been imported with it?

The African was very fond of Mdoor-door because of its yield, easy to shell, and it produced white meal despite having multicoloured grains, but there was a problem. As all the maize grown on the farm by the labourers had to be yellow to avoid stealing, one couldn't be sure if the maize meal in their possession which had white grains amongst it had been stolen. The labour did not like yellow maize to eat but this was overcome by allowing them to exchange any yellow maize for white maize meal.

With a mixture of the three kinds, I produced a cob that was well sheathed, somewhat drought resistant, had a fair depth of seed, was flinty, didn't shed easily, had about 12 rows and had good quality. The selection of seed maize was done during harvest as the maize was put into the crib and also as it was being shelled. All these selected cobs were put into a separate store and a couple of wives of labourers would cut off both ends of the cobs with a panga (chopping knife) and expose the core. Only the ones with a pure white core were retained for shelling with a small hand operated machine. Such seed maize to be used on the sophisticated modern maize planters would have to be graded by size by different machines. I did no grading, it was left to each customer to grade it to his own specification. I think this was the best way, in that any complaints on grading were not my responsibility.

Every year I kept watch on these characteristics and brought in seed to mix with my own to retain this quality. I had some luck with it and I won the country's seed maize competitions for the best results over 3 years in the trials. One aspect troubled me. Why the germination test on five days was poor, and very high on nine days.

Many sophisticated maize planters have been developed, some would punch out 3 or 4 seeds on an area the size of a penny, could be adjusted to drop at intervals, whereby the crop could be cultivated along and across the rows, but this type of maize planter created problems when thinning out to the required plant population. There is an old saying of "One for the rook, one for the crow, one to rot and one to grow." As there were no rooks or crows and the germination was almost 100% this old saying didn't apply.

If the planter was set to cultivate both ways on 40 inch rows there would have to be three plants on each drop for a population of about 11,000, thereby if four seeds were dropped to make sure there were sufficient plants and all the seeds germinated, the plant population was 25% too many, and if one tried to remove the extra one all four would come out as the roots were entangled.

My choice was the two row ox drawn planter that had flat drop seed plates with three quarter inch holes, set to drop every seven inches. Three of these planters were adjusted to 40 inch rows, were attached to a beam and pulled by a small crawler tractor. Super phosphate was applied at 80 lbs per acre and I put on a device that put the fertiliser to the side rather than on top of the seed. I experimented with various rates of fertiliser but as yields could be improved with a higher rate, the cost was not justified. If a high rate of say 240 lbs was applied, the yield was depressed lower than the control rows.

Most farmers created a seed bed by discing, but I considered this a waste of time and cost as it left the soil vulnerable to erosion. Up to about 200 acres were dry planted, always on the contours, before rains, on a very rough seed bed. The clods would be crushed by the planter wheels, and not many weeds germinated on the rough clods when the rains came. Five days after the first rain the whole lot had to be tine harrowed on that day. If left to the sixth day some shoots would be damaged. One had to make sure that all available harrows both for oxen and tractors were ready. In about a week, after germination, a start would be made on hand weeding (hoeing) along the rows of the worst fields with weeds, and two row cultivators attached to two row crop tractors would begin work. Shields were attached to prevent soil covering tiny plants, and progress was very slow at first.

Tractor drivers were instructed to be careful to always follow the pair of rows planted by the two row planters and return on another pair nine or ten ahead and continue advancing with the same turning circle until the patch was finished, and do the same again. This routine was quicker and fewer plants were destroyed on headlands than if the tractor had to stop and reverse to get on the next rows.

Next came thinning out to a population; of 12000 to the acre on good land and between 9500 and 11000 on poor soil. Plant selection was important and it worked out there should be 25 plants every ten yards for 12000, and 22 for the other population. No thinning was done on the 6 row headland as these would be thinned out by the tractors turning on row crop cultivation.

Weed killer sprays were tried with little success. Perhaps it was the early type of weed killer that wasn't compatible with the maize. Recommendations were that it should be applied at 6 to 9 inches high, but even with spray jets directed to the side of the plant to keep it out of the funnels, they still suffered. Some broke off at 5 feet high, just where the anchor roots came out, and others had the top leaves closed up and the tassel could not come free.

I gave up and found the best method to get rid of the weeds was by cultivation and hand hoeing and to aerate the roots with one and a half inch chisel tines set deep. I didn't like the duck foot on wing tines as when the soil was rather wet they would smear.

Wheat Barley and Oats

The drilling of wheat barley and oats would commence in early July on land that had been cultivated two or three times to get rid of the weed, particularly water grass, and would always be drilled on the contour. In the early 1950s there were eight different varieties to choose from that varied from 90 to 140 days to maturity but towards the end of the 1950s this had been reduced to some four varieties even though a lot of new ones had been lost by attacks of black stem rust. Fortunately in the Trans Nzoia we had early warning from farms on the Uasin Gishu Plateau that certain varieties had become suspect and it was not advisable to plant that variety the following year.

There was one variety of wheat that seemed somewhat resistant to the black stem rust, and I wondered if there were other varieties available in the U.K. that had similar characteristics. Several varieties of seed wheat were imported from the U.K. for trials as we were getting desperate for varieties to combat the rust.

They were sown at intervals of about a month and grew well up to the stage of flowering, then all of them died.We did not discover why they died but it was not by black stem rust. It was a big disappointment but if one didn't experiment, nothing would ever be achieved.

The American farmers believe that the spores of this rust are carried into the upper atmosphere from Mexico and they use aircraft and droges to identify the spores. Ours were supposed to originate in Ethiopia and if the spores occurred up to the time the wheat was in flower, no grain at all would be harvested. If later it would be almost worthless shrivelled grains. Up to the time I left the country no sprays for fungicides were available to combat the rust. I have not known it to attack barley or oats.

I experimented with different rates of seeding and found the best to be 80 lbs per acre and the same rate of super phosphate. Just when the wheat was about to tiller, it was top dressed with 120 lbs of nitrogen and rolled. The rolling came about more or less by accident as I rolled one patch that was uneven and had a few roots sticking up, and to my surprise it yielded 2-3 bags per acre more. I am convinced that the result was because the nitrogen had been buried and thereby not leached out by the sun and the wind.

The barley and oats were drilled and fertilised at the same rate and rolled likewise.

Greenfly would attack some of the fields in most years but a spray that was available soon killed them off.

Sunflower

This was grown on certain fields that were not very fertile or the soil was thin or had been eroded. Three varieties were grown, the white, and the black that had a very high oil content, and a striped one that had a very small kernel and a very low bushel weight. The reason for growing this rather useless variety was demand from the American birdseed market. I believe that sportsmen used it to lure certain wild fowl and it could be seen when broadcast on the snow. Only a small acreage would be sown because of harvesting problems that I shall describe later.

The seeding rates were the same as maize with a pip every six inches on forty inch rows. It could also get about 80 lbs of phosphate per acre but no nitrogen. All three varieties were thinned out at 6 inches high to leave a plant population at around 12,000 and were cultivated as maize. I have never known this plant to have any diseases or to be attacked by any bugs, grubs, or worms for anything. It was thereby reliable but on the other hand the returns were poor except the by product by use as cattle food.

Sunflower was marketed mainly through Asian agents who were particular with regard to the colour for export to the shooting fraternity in America for the striped variety. The white and black varieties were sold at a price that was based on the oil content.

Beans

There was a good demand from the Asian community for a small bean that was white in colour, it was known as Njahi. It was very similar to the bean we have in a can with tomato.

As we had to keep the coffee plantation clean I decided we might as well use this operation by inter planting with the beans and hope that the coffee would get some benefit from the nitrogen left by the beans. It was quite successful and easily marketed to the Asians.

Bananas

Bananas were very easy to grow and were very prolific. I don't think there was a market for them as every household, even in towns, would have a small plot for their own use. They were grown purely as additional rations for the labour force.

We had two plots of about an acre each. One was in a river bed and another amongst some rocks, each of which had some shade from trees. They were planted nine feet by nine feet and would produce a lot of suckers from the base and all would be cut off except one besides the one with fruit. When the fruit was harvested the plant was cut down and cut into sections of about a foot long and left as mulch and another sucker allowed to grow.

The two plots would produce about a ton of fruit each week throughout the year and it was much appreciated by the labour force. Monkeys were the only predator that we had to guard against, whereby a house for a man and his family was built nearby. He would do other work on the farm besides guarding the crop, and could help himself and his family to all the bananas they

I am not too sure whether an intoxicating drink can be made from the variety of banana that we grew, but another variety called a plantain that was bigger and didn't ripen to a yellow colour was so used in Uganda. The method used was to dig a hole in the ground, line it with banana leaves, put in the peeled bananas, tread it into a mush and allow it to ferment. I don't know whether they ate the mush or drained off the fluid.

Coffee

As far as I know there are just two varieties of coffee trees or bushes. They are the Arabeka and Robusta and both would grow into trees if they were not pruned. Most plantations were planted in rows of 9 feet with plants 7 feet apart. If the land was level they would be 9 feet apart to enable it to be cultivated two ways. The plantation that I had was about thirty years old and the old stock was about six inches in diameter. From this old stock it was desirable to have four shoots that were spaced evenly around the stock, and each should be one, two, three, and four years old. The youngest one would not bear fruit. After harvesting the old one would be removed and one shoot would be allowed to grow at a point equidistant from others on the stock.. The plantation would be cultivated and kept clear of weeds and some pruning was necessary to the primaries.

No fertiliser was applied but the bushes were sprayed with a solution of copper twice before flowering in late May or early June. It was believed that the copper solution could not be absorbed by the upper part of the leaf, thereby the spray was directed upwards at high pressure

The flower was snow white and about one inch in diameter and would remain until it was wet with rain. Poor rainfall would mean some loss of the crop.

The fruit, known as a bean did not come from a pod as most beans do. It was from a cherry each containing two beans.

Harvesting was commenced in early November when the cherry was blood red, and as they ripened unevenly they had to be picked by hand individually. They were picked by the women at a price of so much per four gallon can full, and care was taken to ensure that all the cherries were ripe.. That same day the harvested cherries were put through a machine that had copper discs and adjustable knives that split the cherry and a flow of water through the machine carried the beans and skin of the cherry through a trough of running water known as a Guatemala Grid. This grid removed the cherry skins and also separated the beans into good and poor grades.

Afterwards the beans were just covered with water and fermented to remove the slime that covered the bean, usually about twenty four hours and thoroughly washed. Then they were fed into drying trays out of direct sunlight, but only one bean deep and afterwards doubled up as they dried out.

When thoroughly dry they were bagged up and sent to the Coffee Marketing Board, where they were hulled (that is, the parchment was removed from the bean) and graded for quality.

The grading sheet (if I remember correctly) had nine divisions for colour and size of the raw bean, and nine divisions on the taste of the roasted bean. That meant a lot of different grades and prices ranging from £200 per ton of poor quality to £600 for the best, whereby it was important that all operations were carefully carried out. For instance, if the knives on the machine for splitting the cherry were too close and damaged the parchment the fermentation would be detected in the taste.

The other variety, the Robusta, was produced in a different manner in that it was allowed to fully ripen on the bush and shook off into a sheet. Most of the coffee that is produced world wide is of this variety. It has a bitter taste but nevertheless is favoured by many nationalities.

Weeds

There were three kinds of grass-type weeds. One was couch grass with a broad leaf, and another with a fine leaf, bluish in colour like wire, and cattle couldn't even eat it. Another, the Kikuyu grass was a kind of couch grass that spread above the ground unlike the other two. It was widely used on lawns as it was bright green and fairly drought resistant and favoured by cattle.

Mexican marigold that had been imported as a garden flower of about 18 inches high had spread everywhere reaching a height of over six feet. It had an abundance of thin brown seeds that must have been full of oil. When set on fire the seed heads seemed to explode. It could smother a crop but only needed a sniff of weed killer to kill it off.

Onion grass was a vigorous plant related to the onion with dark shiny leaves and three cornered stalk carrying the star seed head. It spread by both small onions on the roots as well as the seed. The cattle wouldn't eat it and in the 1950s there wasn't a weed killer to touch it. On one infestation I once counted 40 plants per square foot. It was very difficult to remove by cultivation or hand hoeing if once established in row crops. I found it was not advisable to sow crops on land that had this weed until September, when after many cultivations by harrow or plough, most of the small bulbs would have germinated and been killed off.

Datus stramonium was a bit of a nuisance in maize but a disaster in wheat and barley, as the seed is held in a spiky pod the size of a bantam egg, and the seed was the same size and weight as barley and wheat. and was very poisonous.

It was susceptible to weed killers. If only a very few of these seeds were discovered in wheat or barley the whole consignment was down-graded and very little paid for it. To avoid this happening a labourer was detailed to walk just ahead of the combine and pull out any plants that had emerged after spraying.

Storms

Torrential rain didn't cause much damage to the crops but would cause erosion to land that wasn't terraced or if one hadn't maintained the terraces. Hail usually followed the same path each year and if the maize had just begun to tassel and the silks were not out of the cobs, the seed would not be fertilised and therefore few if any seeds. The tassel would be broken off and the leaves shredded. Most of the farm was off the hail path but one year I had 300 acres of maize badly damaged to yield only about a quarter of the expected yield, and a 50 acre field of barley was flattened to pulp, but it recovered and made a reasonable crop.

Pests

The stalk borer was the worst in maize crops. I believe the adult form was a moth, not that I ever saw one, and it laid its eggs on the first two leaves where they leave the main stalk. It was the duty of the foreman in charge of the gang that were thinning to look out for these first signs. If they were not discovered at this stage the next sign was blemishes on the top leaves as the caterpillar had climbed the stalk and was down the funnel. In both cases a spray was used with just one jet passing over the plant. Occasionally only a strip on the windward side would be infected, then hand labour was used to pour a little disinfectant down the funnel of each infected plant. It was labour intensive but cheaper and quicker than doing the whole field by tractor.

If the caterpillars had not been killed off, they would come out of the funnel and bore into the stalk where they would some time pupate, but the plant was dead and would not yield a cob.

Cut worm was nothing to worry about in that it would cut off a few plants when they were tiny and as we had plenty of plants to be thinned it didn't matter.

Cockchafer bug was one that one could do little or nothing about. It was a big white kind of caterpillar that worked just below the surface of the ground and travelled along the rows killing off the maize even until they were two feet high. They were usually in patches. As it appeared that grass weeds had harboured the adults and I had almost eliminated these, this pest was more or less a thing of the past.

Army worm could be terrible, in that they hatched out as yellow green caterpillars by the million, to the extent that they have stopped trains by their masses on the railway lines. Mostly they would hatch out on grass land and invade the maize fields and then if the tractors were busy spraying outbreaks in the maize I would plough a furrow alongside the field of maize and plough another when the furrow was filled with them, or they were eaten by the thousands of storks that suddenly appeared. The outbreak would usually happen once a year and would last a week but it was hectic while it lasted. Often the maize was only about one foot high and it was not too late to be replanted, but the yield would have been lower.

Desert locust has devastated Africa, the Near East and Middle East for centuries, and only in modern times with the advent of aerial spraying has this scourge been eliminated. To the best of my knowledge the base of the desert locust is in the Arabian peninsula where migrations occur every year, eastwards to Afghanistan, Russia and Pakistan and southerly to Ethiopia. It is believed that if the Desert Locust Control were allowed into the Arabian Peninsula to tackle this scourge at its base the swarms would be thing of the past, but as they are considered a delicacy and a source of food for people of that area no permission has been granted to my knowledge.

I have been told by old soldier settlers of the First World War that the swarms were 40 miles in diameter and almost made day into night. They used to put out old oil and damp vegetation at strategic points in their crops and set them on fire, and with the help of natives making a noise and banging on tin cans hope to drive them off the crops before they had eaten too much. It is said the only vegetation they will not eat is sweet potato tops. I have only seen one swarm of about ten miles in diameter that was about twenty miles away. Quite often there were a few about, and our labour force would catch what they could and eat them as they were caught, without cooking. The Desert Locust Control used aircraft to spray them on the ground at first and later found it was more effective to spray them in flight.

Black grain weevil also caused a lot of damage in grain that was stored. The old type of maize crib and other buildings used for storing wheat and barley had wooden floors and I found it impossible to get rid of them as there were always grains underneath. I therefore took all the floors out and made a bitumen floor. During my first years there was no effective means of control and the Government Marketing Board paid extra for each month that the grain was stored. Naturally some farmers complained that the storage allowance was insufficient and a test was made of one of my maize cribs. It was duly shelled as instructed in May, having been in store since December, and showed a loss of 30%.

When suitable insecticides became available the storage allowance was discontinued. The method I used was to put the required amount of powdered insecticide on each load, and each month during storage, blow in powder from the windward side. No wheat, barley, or oats were stored in bulk and all the bags were liberally dusted as they were stacked and powder blown on maybe twice a month when most of it seemed to have blown off.

Other and Larger Pests

The worst was the small monkey that was blue underneath and when spread eagled on an acacia thorn tree the only part that could be detected was the tail hanging down. They were in groups of 80 to 100 strong and were very clever in that they always posted a lookout and if one was shot, only a few minutes would elapse before they posted another. They were reluctant to cross bare ground so a strip of land about 12 feet wide was mown on the side of the maize field that was adjacent to their habitat in the river bed. It wouldn't have been too bad if they only took what they could eat, but they would break off say ten cobs before they found the one that was satisfactory. That gives an idea how much damage they caused in a few minutes.

The best way to get rid of them was to get an earthenware jar that was used by the natives for water. It had a small hole in the top that a maize cob would just slide into. The jar was wired to a tree somewhere in their vicinity. When the monkey found the maize cob it could not extract it, nor would it let it go. It was fast by the hand. A bag was placed over its head to prevent being bitten and it was painted with all the colours that were available and set free. No monkey could be seen until the painted one joined them after which they were seen everywhere being pursued by the painted one. The natives said they would drop out of the trees exhausted rather than allow this mysterious painted one catch up with them.

Once I had a troop in a river bed that ended in open country, and with the help of about a hundred natives we thought we could shoot most of them. The natives with dogs were put on either side of the river bed to prevent the monkeys from breaking out into the open country and at the end. The rest of them were in the river bed making a lot of noise and throwing sticks into the trees and bushes. I think we shot about eight or ten who tried to break back, and on reaching the end there wasn't one in sight and they hadn't broken out to the sides or the end. We thought it was a mystery and were disappointed and my neighbour remarked that there certainly wasn't one in the tree we were standing by. Looking carefully I found one wrapped round a branch only a yard away and perfectly camouflaged. After that we looked more carefully but of the whole troop we only killed about twenty.

Another monkey, rather bigger but only in troops of six or eight were about in open country, but they didn't seem partial to maize and didn't do much damage.

Colobus monkeys were about in odd ones. They were a spectacular sight with their long black and white hair swinging through the upper branches of the trees faster than we could run on the ground, but did little or no damage to crops.

The baboon fortunately didn't ever pay me a visit although there were a few troops about. I don't know why they had the filthy habit of defecating in water troughs. The stench was terrible and the cattle would not drink. Perhaps it is the custom of baboons to defecate in water so the habit is natural to them.

Leopard were always around and we left them alone although they killed a lamb or a sheep now and again. Their favourite diet was monkey so that the more the better to keep the monkey population down. Often I came across them sunning themselves on a footpath. When seen it was advisable to stop, and while keeping an eye on it, to walk backwards and wait under a tree preferably a thorn tree, and usually in a few minutes it would clear off. The Africans considered it very foolhardy to try to scare them away. They would often attack.

Spotted hyena were about, almost always old ones, though they are generally in packs in the game reserves. I think the odd ones we had were the ones that had been driven out of the packs.

They are scavengers and I have not known them make a kill but they have bitten off the tails of young calves. On one occasion they were being quite a nuisance and I took up position in the calf house to wait for them. It was a moonlit night with a lot of cloud cover and after a few hours one arrived on a gravel path only about twenty yards away, the ideal distance for a 12 bore loaded with either SSG or BB shot. The hyena stopped on the path just as the cloud obliterated it. I waited patiently for it to appear in moon light, but I was disappointed. I thought that a slight movement would have given its position away.

On another occasion I was out shooting deer for the pot. It was an ideal night with no moonlight and hardly any wind. I had a single 12 bore shot gun loaded with SSG or BB and a powerful 5 cell torch. The best method was to walk around the fields until one spotted the eyes of the deer. There is some difference between the different breeds of deer eyes. There are differences of shape and colour. Having shot for the pot for several years I could tell which breed it was before I shot it. However on this occasion I found some eyes I had not seen before. They were almost round and off-white in colour. I felt sure it wasn't a leopard as they are similar to the cat, being round and white. I decided to find out.

My method in shooting deer was to locate them, and then lower the beam of the torch just in front of them, when they would advance a few steps and stamp their feet, and I would continue this until they were about 25 yards away.

I managed to draw this animal to about 30 yards, just short of the 25 yards that would certainly kill it, and then it disappeared. A few minutes later I found it coming towards me from behind and again it stopped out of my desired range. It continued to do this a few more times just out of range and cleared off. I was disappointed but excited at having been stalked instead of being the stalker. As the ground was very wet I had a look for the spoor the following day and found it to be that of a large spotted hyena.

Deer we had were Duiker, Oribi, Bush buck and Reed buck. The oribi was the only one that was in small herds and it was necessary to thin them out every now and again. Up to about half a dozen was nice to see on a field of about 100 acres of wheat but when it got up to 20 it was time to cull a few. The .22 rifle with a soft nosed bullet was very effective.

Porcupine caused a lot of damage to the maize whereby they would chew off a plant long before it had a cob on it. There were several places where they lived, usually an old ant-hill that an ant-bear had partially excavated, they would enlarge it and each build a nest with a store place alongside. There could be three or four entrances and the best way to kill them was to use a 16 bore trap gun directed to the entrance which had the trip wire across it. It would be shot in the head and the other ones inside couldn't get out past the carcase. I have killed up to ten from one of these old ant-bear holes.

Often they came from neighbouring farms and as my crop of maize would be one of the earliest they gave me plenty of attention. Like the wart hog I think they could detect the stage of a crop by smell from a good distance. The method of control was different in that one could not go around other farms siting trap guns. The porcupine always seemed to use the same path from neighbouring farms and would continue on into the maize for a few yards on the same path. This was the place to put the trap guard trip wire but care was needed in that a notice would be displayed to warn that there was a gun there, and its position written down in a notebook. If by any chance its position was not noted and it was lost, one couldn't go looking for it as you could get shot in the legs, the gun being aimed at 9 inches above the ground. The only other way was to leave them until harvest time and flatten the maize to make it discharge and hope it didn't ruin the tractor tyres. Better that than having one leg blown off.

The Africans said that porcupine could shoot out its quills but I could not believe this. As they were a great delicacy and when one prepared them the quills were pulled out rather than being skinned, and the quills were very fast and needed a lot of pulling. But one day on my rounds with two dogs they found a porcupine and during their efforts to kill it one dog ended up with half a dozen quills buried in its rear end. It is difficult to surmise that a dog would reverse into the quills so there is an element of doubt.

Wild pig family. There were the giant forest hog, bush pig, and the wart hog. The last two were around most of the time, but rarely the giant forest pig. The bush pig was an individual and the wart hog in sounders of maybe eight or ten. The damage they caused was like that of the porcupine. I found the answer to forestall them was the electric fence. A strip of grass was mown on the side of the field they were entering, and using a 12 volt tractor battery for a length of two miles. It kept them out as I could see from their foot marks where they had jumped back, but believe it or not they went round the ends and I had to put another one up.

Ant bears. There were quite a lot of ant bears (Aardvarks) which was not surprising by the numbers of anthills that provided them with ample food. They caused no damage to the crops except for digging big holes to feed on the ants. These were to be avoided when cultivating maize and sunflower, and combing wheat and barley. Very often they would dig holes in the middle of the road where one would think there were no ants. Apparently the bears knew otherwise.

Lions. During the fourteen years of farming in the Trans Nzoia there was only one incident with lions that I knew about. It occurred on the farm when three heifers were killed. I went out to have a look and found them about 20 or 30 yards apart, all of them with the heads turned over with the throats turned upwards with fang marks but they were not torn out. A few pounds of flesh were torn out of the rear end. There was the one thing that puzzled me. None of them were lying where they had been pulled down. They were two or three yards away with no drag marks on the muddy field. The African head boy said that the lion always tosses its victim after pulling it down. It is hard to believe that a lion of some 300 pounds or so could toss a beast that weighed nearly twice as much.

As I didn't have a rifle nor the expertise to hunt it down and possibly kill it I went to a neighbouring farmer, also a big-game hunter for assistance, but he was away on safari hunting elephant. Another neighbour could assist and came with his two sons each with a .375 rifle and he had a double barrelled 12 bore shot gun loaded with BB shot and also brought three African trackers.

We followed the spoor to a dam about half a mile away where it had a drink and expected to find it laid up in the surrounding scrub land. It was not to be. We tracked it for about three miles across farm land in the direction of Mount Elgon where it was decided it would be too late in the day before it was located and it would be advisable to bring the Land Rover nearer. Whilst I was fetching the Land Rover they found and killed it in a dense thicket. I was told they found it asleep about 8 yards away with its head obscured, and with one rifle shot on its rear end it gathered itself up and was about to charge when it was blasted with both barrels of the shot gun that brought it down, and another shot behind the shoulder put paid to it. It was a full grown young male lion that had not yet grown its full mane. About a week later the spoor of another lion was found almost on the same tracks as the one we killed but it did not make a kill. They just leave a very persistent smell when it could be detected so much later especially as there had been a few rainy days.

Buffalo. We only had one visit from a buffalo although they were quite numerous in the forests of Mount Elgon only three or four miles away. I think the many fences that had been erected deterred them from straying from their habitat. An African reported that he had been chased by a cow that ran like horse at dusk the previous evening. Along with an African tracker I went to have a look and found that the spoor was that of a cow but with a big difference in that the horns of the fetlock was almost twice the distance from the hoof. After tracking for 200 yards the tracker put his finger to his nose and pointed into a maize field. As we had only a shot gun we decided we had better get out of it. A couple of days later I went to have a look and found it had been lying down only ten yards from where we had been. We were lucky that we hadn't been charged.

Giraffe. On a farm that I knew there was a herd of giraffe, about eight that confined themselves in a paddock of about 600 acres and caused no trouble along with the cattle until sunflower was grown in the vicinity. It was only when the sunflower was in flower that they decided that a change of diet from the leaves of the acacia thorn tree was nice, that they decided to break out. They took the barbed wire fences in their long stride as if they didn't exist.

Elephant. We had no trouble with elephant but the farmers adjoining the game reserve on Mount Elgon had plenty, until they found that if the usual barbed wire fence of about 4 feet was increased to 6 feet and a good clear path about 4 yards wide was made so the elephant could see the fence it was a good deterrent. Maize would break off at ground level leaving the roots and soil, but wheat which was a favourite would be pulled up along with roots and soil. The elephant had an answer to this by putting its foot on it and pulling it against its toe nail, very clever! The result was it looked like it had been cut with a lawn mower.

Vultures. These were around at all times but almost never seen unless there was a dead carcase. Experts on the behaviour of these birds claim that there is a network in the sky of these birds, each of which is in sight of another. This has been achieved by timing the birds as they arrive at a carcase. The interval between the arrivals is always the same. We had a roost on the farm in some tall eucalyptus trees that numbered about one hundred, and as we were having a high mortality rate among the calves that were penned at night, I concluded that they were responsible for all kinds of diseases they were bringing from the carcases and decided to get rid of them. In all I shot about 40 over a period of about a fortnight before they decided it wasn't very safe any more and to my delight the mortality rate for the calves was almost eliminated.

Sparrows. We did experience some damage to the wheat from a small sparrow like bird called the Sudanese dioch. Luckily the flocks numbered a few thousand as against huge flocks of many millions in some parts of the country. Occasionally young boys and girls were employed as bird scarers when damage was becoming too much. It was their normal habit to roost very close together in trees and the Agricultural Dept found this habit of theirs an ideal opportunity to reduce their numbers. Several 45 gallon drums of diesel or paraffin were placed under their roost and wired to an explosive charge, and I understood that millions could be killed in one explosion.

Ants. There were three main types of ants. The white ant that built the anthills, the soldier ants that always seemed to be on the move, and a small one that we called the sugar ant.

The white ants were there in their millions and were very destructive. It was inadvisable to erect a building near to one of their ant hills as they would eat all fabrics, leather and wood with the exception of cedar wood. I have excavated many anthills and found tunnels and caverns, some as nurseries and others producing molds which I think are their gardens for growing food. The queen ant could be found about three feet down in a small cavern six inches long and the sides and floor were smoother than the others. It had a large body about 2 inches long, was unable to move and had a lot of attendants.

When they are devouring the wood and other things they are not exposed, they make a covering over the article with what appears to be mud. The ant has a life cycle of one year that corresponds to the first rains in March when the young with wings emerge from the anthills in millions. They only fly for an hour or so when they fall to earth and the wings drop off. They are quite a delicacy for the Africans and there are two methods that I know of for trapping them. One of them occurs about a month before the rains are due, when a wicker frame is made over a likely anthill.

Over the frame are spread blankets with a small opening to the west. A hole is dug at the opening of about two cubic feet and covered with banana leaves. This is always done in the evening and often the winged ants would emerge. If not the Africans would beat a log lying on the anthill with sticks, to cause a vibration and convince the ants it was raining.

I think that they often would emerge without the beating due to the construction of the wicker frame and blankets creating the right humidity. Some of the tribes said it was the expertise of that tribe, another wouldn't work for them. This method was done by men.

The other method which I think was more successful was always done by women and girls. They would select an anthill, remove all the vegetation and make note of the small holes on it.

CROSS SECTION OF ANT TRAP

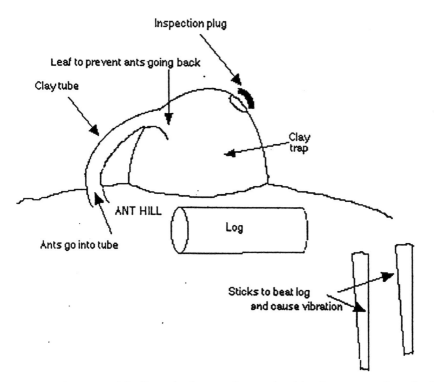

Then they would dig a hole nearby and with the water they had brought with them, make a kind of stiff mortar that they would fashion into pots about six inches in diameter.

They would make a tube from the same mortar, one end of which was placed over a hole they had found, and the other end into the pot where a leaf was placed to prevent the ants returning down the hole. A small inspection hole was made in the top of the pot with a plug. Depending on the number of holes they had found as many as a dozen of these pots would be made. A log was placed on top of the ant hill and beaten with sticks and later the winged ants would emerge, often from a hole they had not found. These were either plugged or a pot was moved over them from a less successful hole. It was done two or three weeks before the rains and some four gallons of ants could sometimes be collected. Many would be eaten alive as they escaped and the ones collected would be cooked.

The soldier ants did not seem to have a permanent home like the white ants. A large number could be found sometimes in a heap of bushwood at the base of a tree, but I don't think it was a permanent base. More likely it was a staging post whilst trekking from one place to another. When one tried to break up a long trail of these regimented ants it didn't take them long to reform and continue on their trek. They had big mandibles and would kill small mammals, lizards etc. that came their way. They were shiny black in colour and their bite was painful.

The small sugar ant was a nuisance as it could get through a very small crevice and was partial to any food that contained sugar. Thereby all food had to be stored in containers that were almost airtight. The meat safe that one had for commodities that could not be stored airtight had to stand with the legs of the safe in small tin cans filled with water. We didn't find an effective way of getting rid of them and had to put up with them.

Mosquitos. We had to contend with these, and always took the precaution of sleeping under nets and taking tablets daily. The family always took the tablets but I don't remember doing so as well, as I wrongly thought I was immune. I had been in India almost four years where malaria was very bad and I noticed the mosquitoes would not sting me, and the Indians said my blood was bitter and I would not be troubled by them. It was not to be. After four years in India and about ten in Africa I got malaria.

Snakes. There were many varieties of snakes about. The one that caused the most casualties was the puff adder. It was two to three feet long, light and dark brown patterned and didn't have a tail, that is a slender rear end. It had the habit of curling up on a footpath while it sunned itself and was likely to be trodden on by a walker who was not observant. There were many in our labour force who were bitten in the ankle or calf and our instructions were for them to kill it and come immediately for treatment. In the early years serum was not available for snakebite and our remedy was to make three or four deep cuts with a razor blade near to where the fangs had penetrated and rub in permanganate of potash. It seemed to work as we never had to rush a patient into hospital together with the dead snake. Later, serum became available that had the dual antidote for the one that coagulated the blood and the other that affected the brain.

A long thin green whip snake that was usually in trees caused a few casualties. The victim would be bitten on the head and shoulders and the instructions if bitten were the same.

Only once did we encounter a big spitting cobra. It appeared in some dense jungle that we were clearing for cultivation, when it raised its head some four feet above ground and spat at them. As a snake can raise only one third of its body it would have been at least twelve feet long. This gang of labourers refused to go back into that area unless one was armed with a shot gun. This was done but the cobra was never encountered again.

Pythons had a home in an outcrop of rocks and their trails could often be seen. One of them paid a visit to our garden one night and the trail was clearly visible on the dew on the grass outside our bedroom window.

One day a gang of pit sawyers reported that a very large python had been seen close to where they were working and had disappeared into a small thicket close by. As there were quite a number of labourers handy we decided to catch it if we could. Even though the searchers were only a few feet apart we couldn't find it. It must have passed through the thicket very quickly and got back to its home in the rocks that wasn't very far away. It was never reported that pythons had killed any animals, but as their diet was small game we wouldn't know.

Farmers and Settlers

I have purposely divided the two for good reason although both were doing the same thing, or at least trying to. In my area there was an Earl, a couple of Dukes, and five Lords, and to add to them were retired officers of the armed services who all seemed to be of the rank of Major or above. Maybe there were others of below that rank who preferred not to use their title. Also there were quite a number of Europeans who came in from India. They had been administrators made redundant when India got Independence, and along with the Lords and Generals would not dream of having dinner without being attired in dinner jackets even though they didn't have guests.

Others had been students of Agriculture College and could have been the sons of "Gentry" and could start farming in Kenya much cheaper than in England, or could have been "black sheep".

I expected to be taught a thing or two by them, as I had never had the privilege of education that is supposed to emanate from the Colleges. Probably they had all the theory and scientific knowledge, but I didn't meet one who could put it into practice. It was pathetic to see the state of some of the farms.

Generally speaking most of them would see that their labour had been put to work and probably visited them to see whether the work was going on as instructed, and by eleven o'clock when it was getting warm, would be off to the Club for a few pink gins before lunch. After a siesta it would be time for a round of golf then on to a party or dinner to end the day. Many of them were not fluent in the language (Ki Swahili) that was generally spoken and had to rely on an interpreter. Often the interpreting left a lot to be desired.

I learned the fairly simple language the hard way very quickly by not having an interpreter, and also had a working knowledge of Jalua, Kitosh, and Bugishu when overhearing their conversation.

I remember once seeing a notice in the Club on a resolution with supporters, that was to be put forward at the next meeting. All but one had a title or commissioned rank, and the odd one out was a Lance Corporal unpaid. I remember him as the best farmer out of the lot of them.

There is also another saying used throughout Africa, "Are you married or do you come from Kenya?"

The ones I regarded as farmers were about equal in numbers to those I regarded as settlers. Most of them were from England under a settlement scheme on vacant plots of land about 1000 acres in extent. There were also a number of Scandinavians, mostly from Denmark, and a few Italians who had been captured in Ethiopia during the war and imprisoned in Kenya, who must have liked the country better than their native Italy.

I had many friends of both nationalities and I found the Danes to have manners that far exceed ours. For instance to be absolutely upright and click heels when shaking hands. Always "Thank you for the last time" when first meeting after having entertained them. On one occasion I was a guest at the showing of a film of the Danish Resistance during the war, and although I was the only one who wasn't Danish, they never spoke a word in their native tongue. If it had been an Africaner assembly it would have been the opposite.

'Good neighbours' doesn't do justice to the help that was given to everyone. Nothing was too much trouble as to loans of machinery or tractors, supervision of their farms in illness or other circumstances, and if by chance a car was broken down on the road, no one failed to stop to see if help was needed.

There were many eccentrics in different ways. One built a large house like a castle with turrets. Another found that all new cars that he bought had something wrong with them, aerodynamically mainly, and he would attach various pieces of tin to the roof and tail end to 'improve' it in that respect, and others would be attached to direct dust away from the doors.

Another was a genius in some ways as he had built a water wheel some twenty odd feet in diameter to drive a generator to supply his electricity needs. He also built a ropeway to cut down transport costs on his farm on the mountainside. Apparently it worked very well provided the African at the base remembered to attach the counterweight. If he forgot, everyone at base had to get out of the way quick or get killed.

Another was concerned with the radio acoustics that were not right in his very large lounge. So he put a speaker high up at one end of the room and about a foot away he hung up a piece of plywood four by four with a hole about one foot in the centre. About a foot from the hole he hung a plough disc about two feet in diameter on some wire. The idea was that sound would come through the hole in the wood, hit the suspended plough disc and vibrate around the room. He considered it a great improvement but I wasn't impressed.

There was one who I think was "well-britched' but had no title, and I think made up for it by having a prestigious car. He was called 'Bwana Majinga' (Mister Fool) by the local Africans because they could call there on pay-day and get paid along with his labour force! He hadn't a clue who worked for him let alone their names. Although I employed four or five times the number of employees

35

that he did, I knew the names of all mine as well as their tribes and marital status.

All the settlers were given nick-names by the Africans, most of them derogatory. Mine was "Bwana Surengu". When I asked the meaning of the word they said it was interpreted as "The master who gets up early in the morning."

It was a fact that I made a start at dawn at about 6.15 a.m. to make any changes in the work ordered the night before should there have been any heavy overnight rain. I still couldn't believe I had been given this distinction but I couldn't extract any other interpretation.

Then there were the Africaners who had migrated from South Africa after the Boer war as they didn't like the British rule there. I think most of them arrived by boat at Mombasa along with their trek oxen and Merryweather wagons, and others came overland.

Most of them settled on the Uasin Gishu plateau, an area of about 1600 square miles adjacent to the Trans Nzoia at an altitude of just over 7000 feet that was flat and fairly free of scrub. It was their El Dorado and the principal town was named Eldoret.

I think that the country was surveyed for settlement in the early 1920s when the first soldier settlers of the First World War arrived, and the area set aside for a township was on the site of this town and was numbered 64 and it was often called as such for many years.

The soldier settlers of the first war said that the Africaner likes to live alone, and if another settler arrived within the horizon they would move to another place as it had become overcrowded.

They were very ingenious and craftsman as to the repair of their wagons, the building of stockades and houses, the making of soaps and the preservation of meat by tearing it into strips, then hot-wind drying it to make their biltong. Generally speaking, most of them in the 1940s and 50s seemed to farm one area for a few years and then move on to another. I think the system was inherited from their forefathers. in South Africa.

Before the branch line of the railway was built to serve the north east of the country, many of the Africaners were engaged in the transport of commodities to and from the railway station at Londiani on the line from Nairobi to Kampala in Uganda.

Some had as many as 30 teams of oxen engaged in this transportation and it is said that in one rather boggy area this trail was seven miles wide where they had tried to cross it.

Top Dressing

The advice given by the Local Agricultural Centre often left much to be desired in that they said it was a waste of money to apply nitrogen to maize, wheat, barley and oats as the crops got all the nitrogen they needed from all the sunshine we had. I could not believe it, and carried out experiments in great detail on dressing crops ranging from 50 lbs per acre to 150 lbs at all three stages of growth and counted the plant populations on each, to cut out any errors, and a good strip of control between each.

Later they were harvested and weighed and evaluated, and I found that 100 lbs per acre applied on maize at shoulder high growth would give 50% more in yield. There was a further increase in yield up to 150 lbs but the cost was not justified. I understand that now that short hybrid maize is being grown up to 300 lbs nitrogen per acre is being used to yield up to 6000 lbs per acre. Our yield was up to 4000 lbs.

As top dressing at shoulder high could not be done mechanically, sample bags were given so that each worker would know how much to apply to the length of the row. After one or two rows they would apply the correct amount without running out or having some left. Only every other row was dressed and the foreman was instructed to look out for suckers that could be growing from the base of the maize plants. Very rarely did these suckers produce a cob with seeds on it so there was no point in growing another stalk and all were removed.

Undersowing

Undersowing with grass seeds was done about the same time and again the labour was given sample bags of seed and soon managed to sow the correct amount of about 20 lbs per acre.

The type of grass seed was Nzoia Rhodes grass. I tried others such as molasses grass but was disappointed with them. There are several strains of Rhodes grass and I produced my own from the grass that was growing wild. One of them had two tiers of seed head and the leaf was much broader than the others. I got the wives and children to collect them and paid them so much per pound if they were all true to type. Ten acres were sown in the first year and soon I had enough to sow the 400 to 500 acres each year and some for sale.

The Agriculture Dept. did trials on our farm with various grasses and clovers and concluded that my type was inferior on palatability but good in production, and I wondered whether to discard it, but the following year when the protective fence was taken down the palatability type was eaten very close and did not recover after the hot dry spell of January to March. I kept my own type. It would have been a disaster if all the 1400 acres of grass leys I had was bare land with 1000 head of cattle to feed.

Maize Harvesting

The old method of harvesting maize was to cut the stalk at the base and stook it early in November. The stooks would be about 6 feet in diameter at the base. Later the husk was removed from the cobs and the cobs bagged up. The only advantage of this method was that some of the land could be ploughed between the lines of stooks and the supervision of the harvesting of the cobs was easier. The disadvantages were that the residue of the crop was all in heaps and would be burned as ploughing these heaps was impossible and that the labour in involved in stooking was in my opinion unnecessary.

Also I disliked to burn this mass of residue from the crop as I consideredthat the soil was very short of humus which would retain moisture as well as prevent soil erosion. Experiments proved beyond any shadow of doubt that this was beneficial to the following crop, as when there was a dry spell, the crop did not suffer, whilst the one without the humus made the miize look like onions. The rotting down of this humus did cause some yellowing of the leaf for a short time, but it soon recovered. It was to be my next experiment to top dress with nitrogen to prevent this happening, but I left the country before I could do it.

The type of maize was ten feet or more in height and subject to being blown down by the winds and the cobs could be anywhere four to seven feet from the ground. Mechanical harvesting was tried but abandoned as too many cobs were left behind. With the shorter hybrid maize with all the cobs about four feet from the ground the harvester works well.

Harvesting the standing crop by hand was carried out for a year or two, but supervision was almost impossible except on horseback. Some would harvest cleanly the maize that was standing and leave the ones lying on the ground, and others would do the opposite. Pulling down the maize along the rows with a thirty foot pole was tried but too many cobs were left entangled in the row, having been pulled down on top of each other.

Thereafter the maize was pulled down across the rows which exposed the cobs for better harvesting, and another advantage was that the maize stalks were lying across the path of the plough which followed the contour.

Gleaning

Even though supervision of the harvest was as tight as possible, some cobs were left behind and it was worth while to glean most of the fields.

Maize Cribs and Shelling

The maize cribs were buildings 11 feet wide, 10-11 feet high and 100 feet long, made of stout tree trunks 9-10 inches thick spaced 4 feet apart and enclosed by wire netting. Some were built in pairs with a 12 foot space between and covered with one roof.

These were useful for stacking shelled maize in bags when storeage was short and when shelling was interrupted by rain.

Parts of the roof could be removed so that they could be filled by an elevator. Eleven feet in width was the maximum that permitted a flow of air through the cobs when they were harvested at a high moisture content.

The capacity of the cribs was about 1300 200 lb bags of maize, a day's work for a Clayton Shuttleworth drum maize sheller driven by an eight nominal steam engine.

When a maize allocation was received during harvesting, the maize would be shelled in the field as it was harvested if the moisture content was below 12%, but most of the crop was shelled in the cribs by a workforce of about 32. There would be 4 either side with shovels, about four pairs with two sacks sewn together to feed the sheller.

Two would pick out the seed maize and pick ear-damaged cobs. Two to man the bagging chutes, four to man the two weighing machines, four or five sewing the bags through the selvedge, the engine driver and stoker, and a couple to look after the shelled cobs, and about six to stack or load lorries.

As I could produce a good sample by this machine, especially when driven by the steam engine that kept variations in revolution to a minimum (unlike a tractor) most of the crop was for export for cornflakes or distilling for whisky.

Sunflower Harvesting

Sunflower had been sown on blocks of 12 acres or so at 2 or 3 week intervals but not later than mid June, so that most could be harvested before the maize harvest in November.

The so-called Russian method was used when about two thirds of the ends of the seed heads had dropped off most of the crop. These were cut off at a slope by a sisal knife at about 2 feet 6 inches from the ground and the heads cut off and stuck on top of the cut stalk.

The heads were stuck upright with black and white varieties and inverted with the striped variety as the colour had to be preserved and not weathered like the others. A gang of about six would cut them in a week and the few that were not ready to cut would then be ripe.

They would be left for up to three weeks or more until completely dried out and then two rows would have the heads bagged and six left. As I didn't have a tipper trailer, a flat trailer with an eighteen inch loose frame was put on it. A gang of six, three either side would throw the heads into the trailer and empty the bags of the two rows.

They were taken to the homestead site where a smaller tractor driven maize sheller was set up and pulled off the trailer by the loose frame.

The drum of the maize sheller was set fairly wide so as to leave the small seeds at the centre of the heads that had no kernel and would improve the sample.

The threshed heads were put through a hammer mill without a screen and blown through ordinary 3 inch water fall pipes into home made silos about 10 or more feet high for cattle feed during the dry months.

The striped variety that had been placed upside down were threshed as soon as possible as parrots would be feeding on them and would knock out much more seed than they ate.

The shorter small headed variety was tried in the hope that it could be combined, but abandoned because of uneven ripening and the loss of seed waiting for them to do so.

The three varieties I grew would be about 10 feet tall and the average size of head about 10 inches. If the plant population had been too low, a number of heads would be on each stalk, and if too high the heads would be small and neither suited our method of harvesting.

Combine Harvesting of Wheat, Barley, Oats and Rye

The combine harvester unit was a 12 foot cut Massey Harris Bagger as there were no facilities for bulk grain storage or transportation in the 1950s.

As most of the land was terraced to avoid soil erosion, the harvesting had to be done on the contour, and the opening cut on each terrace was made on the lower side of the terrace making sure that the corn was cut to the top of the terrace bank. The next cut would be the cut at the bottom of the terrace and maybe of say only 8 feet. The rest of the cutter bar was over the first cut and thereby no heads were nipped off.

Some of the land was fairly steep and the grain on the riddles would automatically flow to one side. Dividers were used to ensure that most of the area of the riddles was in use to prevent grain being carried over with the chaff. The dividers supplied with the machine were often too small and others were made and sometimes an extra one would be added. The 200 lb bags were sewn through the selvedge.

The bags were dropped off in rows and carted to the main store which was the same design as the maize crib, and stacked 8 or 10 high with a space of say 6 inches between. Long poles were laid on each layer so that they wouldn't topple over or touch each other. That enabled dusting with insecticide to be more effectively carried out. As the grain weevil was a serious menace the bags would be dusted every three or four weeks until disposed of.

Farm Houses and Staff

I don't remember any architects being engaged in the design and construction of houses whereby there were many that could be described as odd.

Almost without exception they were built on an elevated position as near the centre of the farm as possible and the front of the house would have the best panoramic view, regardless of prevailing winds or geographical aspect. As they were situated one degree north of the equator there was nothing to lose.

They were all bungalows with at least four bedrooms, a large lounge, dining room, kitchen, storerooms, bathrooms, toilets etc. and a verandah of some twelve feet or more around most of the house.

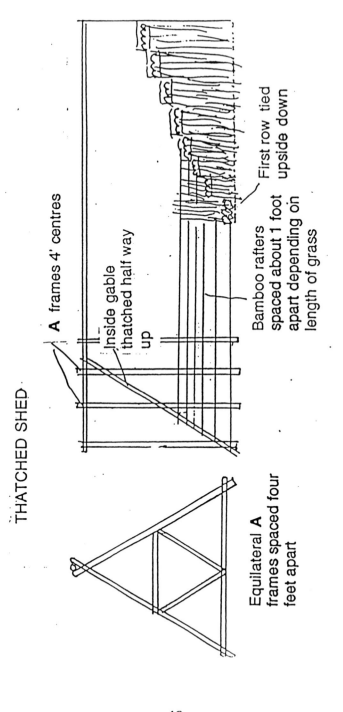

THATCHED SHED

A frames 4' centres

Inside gable thatched half way up

First row tied upside down

Bamboo rafters spaced about 1 foot apart depending on length of grass

Equilateral A frames spaced four feet apart

The rooms were much bigger than normal and the ceilings about two feet higher.

Hand made bricks could be made on most farms and were used in the construction, and lintels were mostly of hardwood. Lime or cement was not used in building the walls. Top soil from the first foot of soil that contained some fine roots was dug, well watered and puddled by the feet of the builders until of the right consistency.

The outside walls would have some of this soil mortar scraped from the joints and pointed with cement. Inside walls were plastered with a mixture of soil mortar and cow dung that was readily available in the pens used for holding the cattle by the cattle dip. The mixture was about 2 parts mortar and 1 part cow dung.

The floors were mainly of cedar which was cheap and available from the saw mills in the cedar forest at altitudes of eight to ten thousand feet. Odd ones were of podocarpus, a semi hardwood that was also cheap and available locally but not as attractive as cedar. The floors of the kitchen store rooms and verandahs were of cement that was treated with a red wax polish that gave a good shine.

The roofs were mainly corrugated iron, often coloured green and later ones had asbestos tiles. Really old ones were of thatch and if the African oat grass (that was the best) was cut at thecorrect time just before the seed was ripe, it would last for up to twenty years.

All these old houses didn't have ceilings and were quite cool during hot weather. Another advantage of the thatch was there was no noise during heavy rain or hail storms. The houses with corrugated iron and asbestos roofing had ceilings of plaster board or wooden match boarding that did little to insulate from this noise.

The house, lawns, gardens of some two to three acres were enclosed in a good fence with a gate to the drive, but didn't have any security devices fitted as found in most farms in South A

It was the custom that none of the labour force other than those directly employed in the household could enter the compound unless escorted by the farm policeman. I think this custom is received from the tribal custom, as the Chief's Compound was out of bounds except by invitation and escorted.

Vegetable gardens if irrigated and well managed by a competent African gardener could keep the household supplied with fresh vegetables throughout the year. The same almost went for the orchards, as apples and oranges would grow alongside each other together with paw-paw, pineapple, guava, banana and other tropical fruits.

The staff I think was related to the systems that had prevailed in India for a couple of centuries, but not just as extensive. Normally there would be a cook, houseboy (not actually a boy) a gardener and a young boy to help around the kitchen, mainly washing pans and keeping the wood burning stove supplied with fuel, and a night watchman. If a family had small children a girl or ayah would also be engaged to keep an eye on the children and do the washing.

Long white gowns were supplied to the cook and houseboy together with a cap similar to a fez. It was the usual practice that the houseboy did not wear any footwear during his duties in the house or serving at table, but on one occasion we had a very good houseboy with very sweaty feet who left footprints all over the highly polished floors, and rather than dismiss him we broke with tradition and supplied him with suitable footwear.

There is another custom which I think was tribal rather than imported with the Indian systems, in that when presenting or serving with one hand, the other hand with fingers outstretched was placed across the forearm of the serving hand. I understand that was done so that the surplus hand could not be used offensively.

As our diet and cooking have no resemblance to African ways, good cooks were in very short supply and a lot of time had to be devoted to teaching them. I remember one cook we had always served rice pudding that was curdled and we could not understand why it always happened, and needless to say we didn't eat it. Then we discovered he added lemon juice to it. I don't know whether he had been taught to serve it that way by a previous employer. He knew we wouldn't eat it and he liked it that way himself.

It did not happen to us, but to many others, that a roast fowl was served already stuffed. Pehaps it is the custom of the African that they prefer to roast their fowls complete with innards, as we do a snipe.

All the game that we often killed for the pot was skinned, or it would have been served with the skin and hair on it, as it was their method of roasting game. We shouldn't pooh-pooh this custom as no doubt it would prevent one particular side of the joint being charred, but on the other hand I am not too sure whether the flavour would be better by the smoke from the hair or wool.

44

During the last ten years we never had to go to the butcher for meat, we had a good supply of all kinds. We killed a pig now and then as a variation in our diet, and on one occasion the surplus was given away to the Africans, and one of them cooked a piece over an open fire as was usual with most kinds of meat, but the large amount of fat that dripped on the fire set his thatched house on fire and burnt it down. He didn't get any sympathy from his neighbours, who said he should have asked them how to cook it, as the only way to cook meat from a pig was to boil it.

With only a few exceptions did the cook have access to the food store. Usually all ingredients that were needed for the menus on that day were issued after breakfast. The servants of the household were issued with the same rations as the farm workers.

Water supply was a problem in certain areas and they had to rely on rainwater from the roofs except the thatched ones. Usually a header tank about twelve feet high was erected and filled by hand pump from the rainwater tanks to supply the bathrooms and kitchen etc.

Hot water was supplied by an ingenious system using a forty gallon drum heated over a firebox near to the supply tank and the supply was connected to the lower part of the drum and from a blow-off pipe at the top that was higher than the supply tank and a pipe was led off this one to the kitchen and bathrooms.

Other farms with a permanent stream or a dam would pump water up to the storage tanks. Others would instal a hydram if the terrain or wall of the dam was sufficient to drive it.

Very few homesteads had electricity, these few having a Lister Startomatic which would start up with the first switch and stop when the last one was switched off. The lighting was by paraffin lamps that needed to be occasionally pumped up to keep a good light.

I tried to teach the Africans to start up these lamps with methylated spirits but to no avail. The globes would be stained with smoke, and paraffin everywhere. The methylated spirits seemed to disappear as fast as the paraffin. They had found a better use for it than lighting paraffin lamps!

As there was no electricity the fridge was paraffin operated, the radio by batteries, and ironing of the best materials was done by a paraffin pressure iron, again one that was beyond the African.

They did the ordinary ironing with a charcoal burning iron. As there were no electric gadgets that are common in households today I think that the number of staff employed were necessary.

Earth Dams

One did not have too many dams made from the earth, and practically all the farms that I knew either had a stream flowing through them, a depression, or a stream on the boundary.

Full marks must be given to the surveyors, when the farms were of different sizes in order that sufficient water was available. Unlike Australia where all the farm boundaries are north and south and east and west.

It was obvious that when choosing a site, that there was a catchment area above it that was big enough to hold water for the number of cattle that would graze the area.

Rather than just keep dumping soil in the depression or bed of a stream. I found that the best way was to mark out the dam base with pegs. If the wall of the dam was to be 15 feet high, that would be multiplied by five and to that would be added the width of a roadway (say about 10 feet), and the base would thus be 85 feet long. The five factor is because the inner wall of the dam would have a slope of one in three, and the outer wall of one in two. The idea was that the wall was stronger by a shallower slope on the inside by the fact that the water was lying on it rather than pushing.

This was a theory firmly believed and practised by early makers of dams and proved by the test of time. Hydraulic engineers may differ on this theory but I have my doubts whether a smaller embankment using less soil, and cheaper to build, would be as safe as the one described.

All the soil from the dam was taken within the dam by ploughing with an ox drawn plough and scooping it up by nine cu. feet dam scoops. I found that one plough could loosen sufficient soil to keep going six dam scoops pulled by teams of six oxen each.

When a dam was built in a depression the work would have to be done during the rains as the soil had to be damp to be compacted by the hoofs of the oxen. When compacted on the bed of a stream, the stop cock could be closed and part of the area flooded so that damp soil could be scooped during dry weather.

Whilst it was being built it must be decided which end of the wall of the dam would have the spillway, and this soil used on the dam wall. The spillway always seemed to be much bigger than seemed necessary, and it was about three feet lower than the wall of the dam, but it was so built that no heavy rainfall would ever flow over the wall of the dam or it would be washed away.

During the later years I was there most farmers hired a contractor to build the dams using earth moving machinery and a sheeps foot roller for consolidation. It was done much quicker but was much more expensive in comparison with one built by oxen, and the consolidation was poor in comparison.

DAM CONSTRUCTION
Not to scale

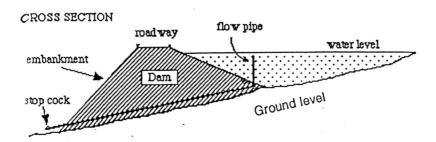

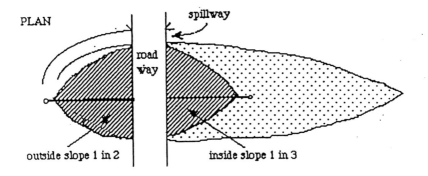

Cattle

I had two breeds of cattle, the local native type, rather small of about 10 hundred weight, of a wide range of colours with medium length of horn, and there were the boran that were bigger, up to 12 hundred weight, were polled, and light brown in colour with a large dewlap.

All the European breeds were there plus a few more of

47

African origin. A booklet was issued by the Veterinary Dept. of the Government that was useful to give instruction in doing postmortems as all the diseases were fully described with what internal organs looked like in relation to each disease. When doing a postmortem it was advised first to cut off an ear and if the blood was like tar, do not skin it, but burn the carcase right away as it could be anthrax.

Otherwise skin it and examine a gland in the shoulder and another just forward of the hind leg about six inches below the hugging bone. If either of these glands were swollen and fluid was present, it denoted tick borne disease known as East Coast Fever.

Then it was best to cut all the ribs on one side of the backbone with an axe, cut along the belly, and the side would fold back like a book and enable one to examine each organ in turn that had not been disturbed by the normal process of gutting. If no disease could be detected from the various organs, the brain was removed and slides taken for examination by the Veterinary Dept. of Government and it was usually diagnosed as haemorrhagic septicaemia.

East Coast Fever was the worst. To prevent this all cattle and calves from two weeks old were dipped in an arsenic based fluid. There were other kinds that were not so poisonous, but just not so effective. During the heavy rains they were dipped every fifth, fifth, and fourth days, leaving Sundays free for work oxen, with which a slight risk was taken but unavoidable as it was the only day free for them.

The dip shown in the diagram held four thousand gallons and was tested for strength of the solution each week and adjusted accordingly. Six or seven herdsmen were used to dip them.

Two would force them in single line through a foot bath, one would control them going in and ensure that only one was in the dip at a time, or some could be drowned. One would stand at the end of the dip with a long pole with a hook on the end, pull out any beast that had somersaulted and ended wrong way round, or was upside down. These animals were noted and given an antidote of one third of a bottle of photographic hypo topped up with water, which was always available.

Another one or two would man the draining pens and operate the two-way gate. No cattle were allowed out of these pens until they were drip dry, as the solution would poison the grass and then one would have arsenic poisoning instead of East Coast Fever.

48

CATTLE DIP

Not to scale

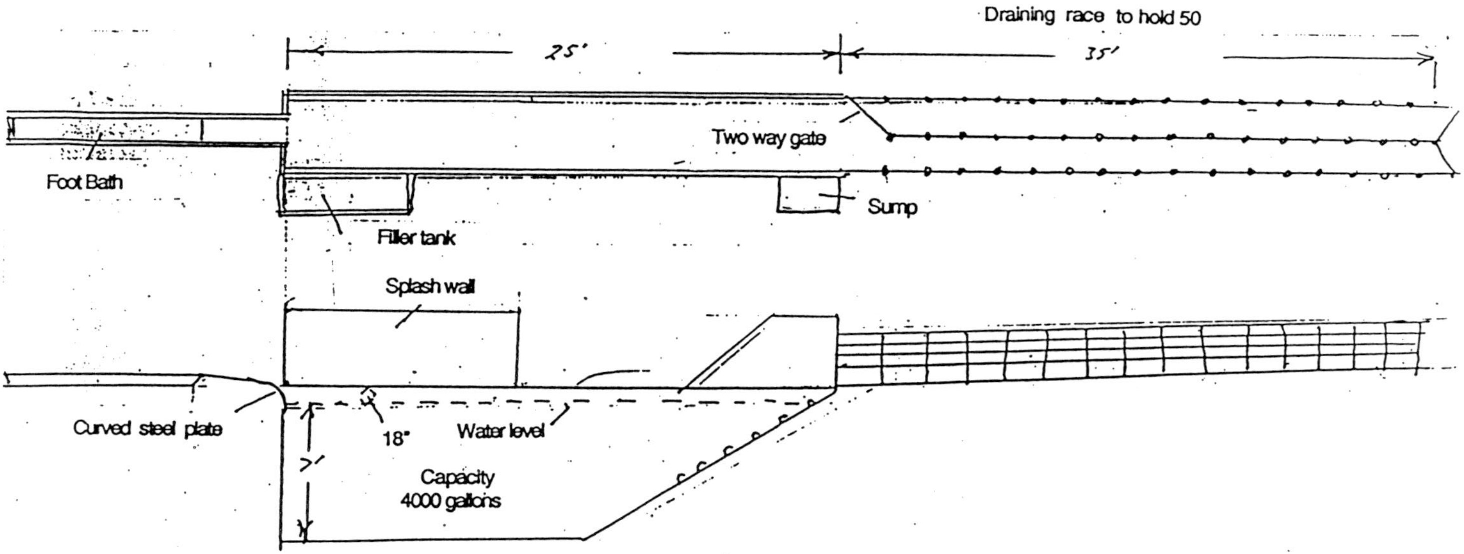

Draining race to hold 50

Two way gate

Sump

Filler tank

Splash wall

Foot Bath

Water level

18"

Capacity
4000 gallons

Curved steel plate

15'

25'

49

During the dry season the dipping times were extended to ten or even fourteen days.

Liver fluke was also a problem in the early years until I virtually eliminated it by scattering sulphate of copper (I think it was copper) in the grass on the waterline of the dams and also around the springs. We dosed for liverfluke with carbon tetrachloride at a certain number of ccs. according to body weight. As this was only a small amount of tetrachloride it was diluted with cooking oil to try to avoid either over or under dosing. If the liver of the beast was badly damaged by fluke it would die in a very short time, but it was considered better dead than alive as it would never do any good.

Foot and mouth disease was endemic in the country. There were three types, A, O, and E. The E type was supposed to be of South African origin and was considered the worst of the three. The effects on the cattle were minimal except in very dry weather when the grass was dry and then it was only the young calves that suffered the most, and they could have a mortality rate of some ten per cent. I have not known any adult native breed of cattle die as a result of this disease.

Efforts were made to prevent the spread of this disease, but this proved useless as the game would carry it from one herd to the next. We found the best way was to spread the disease as quickly as possible. This was done on the day they were dipped. Two or three hunded weight of salt were put in small heaps, and the infected herd came first to drop their infected saliva all over it. In a matter of a few days all the cattle were infected and for three or four days they wouldn't eat much, until a new skin had grown on their tongues. The effect on their hooves was minimal, a few were lame but only about one in a hundred would lose one or two horns off their hooves.

Apart from the game that spread the disease I think that the Kaverondo Crane was responsible for spreading disease more widely, as often outbreaks could occur several miles from an infected herd. These colourful majestic cranes would congregate around watering places for cattle many miles apart.

Vaccine was available for each separate type but, as identification of type was done at Pirbright in England, and as it took more than a week some farmers with pedigree imported herds would inoculate with all three to be on the safe side, as their imported herds were much more affected than the native herds. As the cost was 50 pence for each dose, it was a justifiable expense for valuable imported cattle but in no way could be justified with fairly cheap almost immune native type cattle.

I believe the big ranchers with several thousand head of cattle would get worried if they didn't get the disease after about four years clear, as they would be losing immunity and take steps to introduce the disease.

Salt

This was an important diet of the cattle as indeed it was to the human population. Whether this deficiency was caused by the lack of the mineral in the foods that were eaten, or by the climate I did not know. The 1000 head or more of the cattle would consume at least about 400 lbs of salt each month and it didn't seem to vary much during the dry and wet seasons.

On the farm there was what was known as a salt lick. This was a depression at the base of a small hill that was about an acre in size and about five feet deep. Most of the year it contained water about a foot deep, which I think emerged from some underground strata. Some pieces of elephant tusk were found in it and trails leading from this depression were four or five feet deep and would be the result of thousands of game and elephants that had licked and consumed the mud and water over thousands of years. Just how many tons of soil were removed from this depression I have not calculated but it must be into thousands of tons.

These salt licks were few and far between and of various sizes, maybe due to the amount of salt that extruded from underground springs.

The area on the farm was surrounded by crops and could not be available for cattle for most of the year, and when they were allowed to use the salt lick it was a mad rush accompanied by bellowing and they would drink the muddy water until they looked as if they would burst. I thought I was giving them plenty of salt so there must have been some other mineral or trace element that they required.

Marketing

Maize and wheat were scheduled crops and each year before the crop was planted, the price was fixed by the Government provided that the quality and moisture content was of a certain standard. This I believe was based on a yield of eight bags of maize and five bags of wheat per acre, whereby the producer could make a living. If yields could be produced in excess of this figure, a good profit could be made as the costs of ploughing, cultivating etc. would be the same with the exception of harvesting. I believe advance payments could be obtained by the producers, but to what extent I am not sure as I never took advantage of the scheme.

Barley was bought by the brewing industry if the sample was good enough for them, otherwise it was sold to the local pig farmers. The small quantity of oats was sold locally to the ones with horses, and dairy farmers.

With the exception of small local trade, all the beef was sold to the Meat Commission with slaughtering facilities in Nairobi. The price of all the different grades was fixed annually, which gave the producer a particular grade to produce in relation to the type of stock, breed, and the enviroment on his farm.

The imported breeds of beef animals such as Hereford, Angus, Red Poll etc. commanded the best prices and would mature in two years but one could not expect them to do well or even survive on the indigenous vegetation and poor water supplies.

The native breeds were a lot hardier but very slow to reach maturity at about four to five years. The work oxen could be worked for a lot of this time and still be graded as well as the ones that hadn't.

Allocations were applied for quarterly each year, and if by chance some of the animals were not marketed as applied for, they had priority in the next quarter. The system worked very well. they were always in such numbers as would fill a railway truck.

Brick Making

With the exception of volcanic loam, nearly all the farms had soil with some clay content that would produce bricks. When excavating for this material near a stream, about a foot of topsoil was removed and a working surface of say ten feet was dug. Often below this depth the material contained too much sand. This soil dug out was well watered and puddled by the feet until it was of the right consistency for molding. The molds were of two kinds. One of two bricks and the other of three. The small ones of two could be carried by juveniles, and were oversize of the finished brick to allow for shrinkage that was in the proportion of three eighths of an inch for a nine inch brick and other sizes in relation to that.

Some brick molds were made with a strip of metal on the edges to prevent wear but as the metal was always being worn away and the operator cutting his hands, I made them of hard wood and replaced them more often.

The mold was put on a flat piece of wood and filled with the puddled clay and surplus struck off with a piece of wood. The mold was turned edge up and the piece of wood slid off. It was then carried to the drying area that was clear of vegetation and level, and gently slipped from the mold in rows. If there was a good drying wind or alternately a threat of rain, these molds would be covered with long grass that had been cut in readiness.

PUG MILL

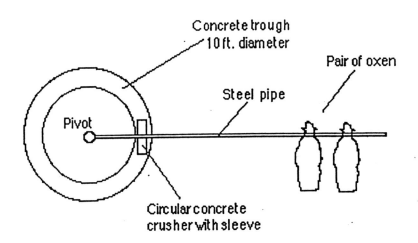

Concrete trough
10 ft. diameter

Pair of oxen

Steel pipe

Pivot

Circular concrete
crusher with sleeve

Not to scale

The following day they could be stood on edge, and as they dried they would be stacked up to ten or twelve high with a space between each and always protected by grass from the sun and rain. It was important that they dried slowly to prevent them cracking when they were burnt.

About thirty five thousand were burnt at a time when they were thoroughly dry. That made a clamp some 20 feet by about 15 feet and 5 feet high and all the bricks were stood on end. Four tunnels were made at the base running lengthwise along the clamp for firing, soil was piled up along the sides and the top covered by the long grass that had been used to cover them when drying out.

The firing took the best part of two days, being continually stoked from both ends of the firing tunnels and after about a week they were cool enough to handle and stack in blocks of of one thousand.

If they had been burnt properly they would give a high pitched ring when tapped with a knuckle. If undercooked it was a dull sound.

To avoid paying for cracked or half bricks or poorly burnt ones, it was the custom to select one of the blocks of a thousand, discard all the faulty ones if any, and deduct the same number from all the rest of the blocks. This work was always done on contract by a known African or one who had been recommended and a price per thousand was agreed and usually a two hundred pound bag of maize meal for four thousand bricks. He was not given the supplementary rations that were given to the farm labour.

Roman Tile Making

As more and more land was cleared and brought into cultivation, suitable thatching grass became very scarce and an alternative had to be found. Corrugated iron was cold and noisy with hail and heavy rain so I decided to make some Roman tiles.

There was one place on the farm where the clay was suitable for making earthenware vessels that the Africans used for water. A few of these were made and fired in an experimental kiln that proved that the material was right, but firing and previous drying was at fault. A thatched drying shed was built that excluded any wind from blowing through, making the drying very slow but preventing them having small cracks. Wooden molds for these tiles could be purchased, but some were too thin and easily broken, so I made them from five eighths square iron welded at the corners.

The clay that was used was from a seam only two feet deep underlying about two feet of top soil and was well puddled in a pug mill to the right consistency and left a couple of days before being molded.

A small table was sanded to prevent the clay sticking, the mold laid on this with a piece of fine wire attached to it. The mold was firmly packed and the surplus struck off with a piece of wood.The piece of wire was then pulled around the mold so that it

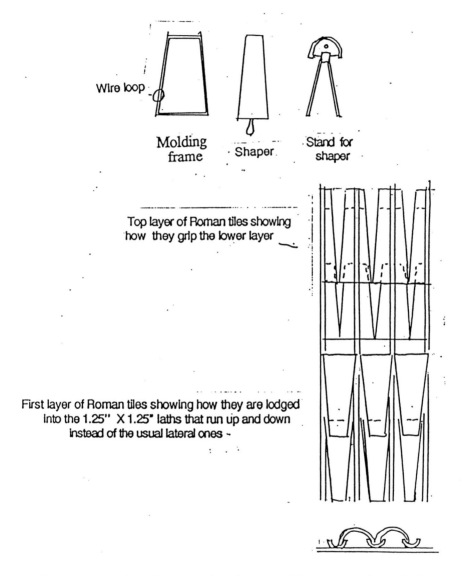

Wire loop

Molding frame

Shaper

Stand for shaper

Top layer of Roman tiles showing how they grip the lower layer

First layer of Roman tiles showing how they are lodged into the 1.25" X 1.25" laths that run up and down instead of the usual lateral ones -

could be removed, otherwise the clay would have stuck to it. It was then slid off the table with the piece of wood on to a shaper. This former was placed on a stand that was narrower and the clay was molded to the former with a slight pressure of a hand that was dipped in a muddy mixture. This slight pressure made the clay expand a little to just overlap the shaper. It was then put on the

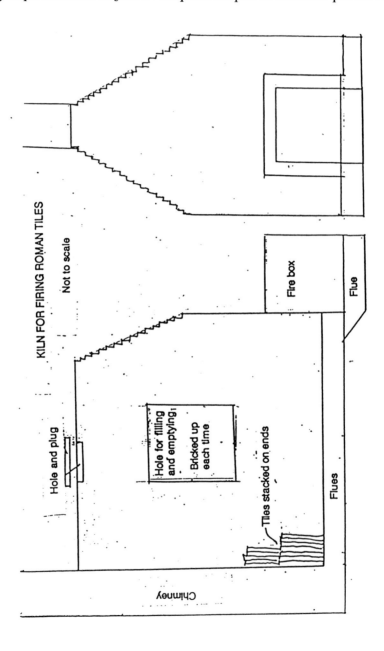

KILN FOR FIRING ROMAN TILES

Not to scale

Hole and plug

Hole for filling and emptying, Bricked up each time

Tiles stacked on ends

Chimney

Fire box

Flue

Flues

56

flat surface of the drying shed, and if the mold had been expanded enough and the clay was of the right texture the former could be removed without it collapsing. They would be laid down in a row for three or four days until firm enough to stand on end, and depending on the dry conditions of the weather would be three or four weeks to be thoroughly dry and ready for firing.

The kiln I built, was a combination of the three types that I saw, and burnt tiles quite well after having teething troubles with the draught. I hoped that the wood fire would burn very well through the kiln and up the chimney, but that was not to be. So a hole was made in the top of the kiln to get the fire going and also to expel any moisture from the kiln and tiles, and then it was closed trapping the heat, and the cold air naturally went to the bottom and up the chimney.

The kiln was fired for four days, maybe three would have been enough, but as there was plenty of fuel the risk of undercooking tiles wasn't justified. When properly burnt they had a high pitched ring when tapped with a knuckle and were light red in colour.

It was noticed that they were somewhat porous on the tiled roofs but not to the extent that rainwater would drip off inside, so I experimented with glazing with salt.

This didn't work as I believe that temperatures of some 1300 degrees are required and I think that the kiln only reached about 800 degrees.

Another attempt was made to make them less porous by painting them with some kind of oxides (I forget which one) and this was successful. Even when only a strip three inches wide was painted on the inside of the underside of the tile, the cost did not justify the benefits of the glazing.

These tiles were not big enough to ensure a good seal on the ridges, so a larger tile was made slightly thicker of the same design to make a good ridge tile.

To make them more attractive the thumb was used to smear the thick end of the tile that could be seen on both the inside and outside of the roof.

I have seen many Roman tiled roofs in Italy, Greece and Turkey but they did not seem to fit as well as the ones we made. As it is labout intensive we could have had an advantage in Africa or on the other hand pride in the workmanship, or even supervision! As they were not fixed to the roof they were held in position by being wedged in the rafters and clamped to one another and a pitch of 28 degrees was enough to stop them slipping and even adequate to run the rain off.

The Farm School

Very few of our large labour force had had any education. To the best of my knowledge there were only two, the farm clerk and the storeman out of the hundred and eighty regular employees. They decided they wanted a school for their children, and a brick building with a thatched roof of 12 feet by 40 feet was built. Schoolmasters had to be approved by the Education Authority, but there was no funding by the Authority for the cost of the building, the basic furniture, and the various items to aid teaching, or the wages of the schoolmaster.

All the necessary items were purchased, a schoolmaster engaged, and some forty children attended the day classes, and twenty or thirty adults attended classes after work. It wasn't necessary for me to enforce attendance, the Headman and the 'wasai' (the elders) were very keen on education and the fact that it was free enforced attendance. Occasionally they would report to me that a certain person was defying them and demand that he should be fined for refusing to comply with their orders.

Sick Parades

Sick parades were a daily occurence held near our house at about 8 a.m. and were examined by my wife who had some nursing experience and qualifications. We kept a stock of various medicines and ointments and bandages, and if the treatment we gave failed to give any relief to their complaints, or they were seriously ill we would take them to the hospital that was about ten miles away. Ulcers on the shins were very common, and even the hospital had difficulty in curing this disease. If we had known that honey was the best cure it would have saved a lot of discomfort and ointments, as honey was freely available. Often they would ask for a 'sendano' that meant an injection by a needle, and they seemed to believe it held some white man's magic. Most of the cures we believed were due to giving them confidence in what treatment was given, rather than the ointment or medicines.

All the labour who reported to the sick parades were entitled to pay and rations if proved unfit for work. A few tried to get a few days holiday with pay by pretending they were ill.

Bees and Honey

I did not know of any European who was a commercial bee keeper. I had one hive, but the African exploited the large number of bees that were about very effectively.

The hives they made were very ingenious. They were about 15 inches in diameter and about four feet long and made from rings of twigs surrounded by bark of trees that was held in place by vines and smeared with mud. They were in two sections held in place by four sticks that were the full length of the hive. Usually they were placed in trees some ten feet or more from the ground and always at a slope of about 30 degrees. About twenty I have seen on the farm, but there could have been many more that were obscured in dense thickets. February was the month they took the honey by removing the upper section and replacing it by one already prepared. They didn't have any veils, clothing or mittens to protect themselves, but used a lot of smoke to subdue the bees and only got a few stings.

The African bee is renowned throughout the world for its bad temper which I found out when I took off my first lot of honey. I got myself well protected from them and used a lot of smoke and was careful not to cause any vibration when I lifted the shallow crate off the hive.. The bees poured out of the hive very bad tempered and covered my veil so that I couldn't see out. The smoke had not had any effect at all. I waited a while still using the smoke hoping that they would calm down, but it was not to be. I retired to our bathroom taking thousands of bees with me and sprayed them with fly killer. If I had not been protected I'm sure it would have been a rush to hospital for an injection.

As the material I had used to create smoke did not subdue the bees like the smoke the Africans used, I think they must have used a certain variety of grasses or leaves that subdued them. They didn't disclose what it was, but I suspect that it was the plant they were forbidden to grow, i.e. hemp.

Despite my unsuccessful attempt at gathering honey, I carried on but used a safer method by spraying fly killer into the hive and blocking them in at night. An hour of so later I took the hive apart when the bees were all dead and left the contents exposed overnight, and found that all traces of the flyspray had evaporated overnight and there was no tainting of the honey.

There must also have been no trace of the fly spray left in the hive as another swarm of bees once reoccupied the hive the following morning, before it was cleaned and reassembled.

Usually the hive would be occupied by another swarm within three days, there were so many swarms about.

Beer, Distilled Spirit, and Drugs

Our labour force were very fond of beer which was made from fermented maize meal. We tried with reasonable success to control the amount being brewed by giving written permission for a maximum of four gallons to be brewed by any adult once a month, provided his previous applications for brewing had not caused any trouble.

I think it took about a week to ferment in a big earthenware pot and the grains of maize were not sieved from the liquid. The method of drinking was not from a vessel or cup, it was sucked from the pot by means of a hollow vine called a 'muridger'. Each of them had his own, that was about six feet long and about half of it was suspended from the roof. They would all sit in a circle around the pot and they kept up some movement of the long vine which I think was to prevent it being blocked by the grains of maize. Blowing down the straw to clear a blockage while the end was in the pot was forbidden.

The local police would sometimes visit the farm and if they were found brewing beer without written permission, or the quantity was in excess of the amount granted, they would be prosecuted and fined.

My neighbour was having a lot of trouble with his labour over violence and drinking parties, and suspected that illegal distilling was the cause. On one particular week end quite a number of my labour asked for passes to visit his farm. I telephoned him to say a big drinking party was to be held.

He suggested that I should join him and make a raid on houses that were supect, but I declined because I believed we should find more trouble than we had bargained for, and advised him that the local police be informed and requested to raid his farm. The raid proved to be quite violent with a few police and labourers injured and during the course of which a rifle was stolen from the police and reinforcements were called to recover it. The event lasted all night long until the rifle was recovered.

About four miles away there was a kind of public house where beer was sold to the Africans near the Police Station on Sundays. On one occasion it was reported that one of our labourers was dead drunk and wanted to use our light lorry to bring him home. He was brought to our house and appeared dead drunk, his pulse was alright and he was breathing normally, but when my wife opened an eyelid he was up and ran off like a hare. I suppose his ruse was a good idea to get a lift back home.

The distilling of spirits from a concoction of various ingredients that had been fermented, was regarded as a serious offence and a jail sentence was often imposed by the local magistrate. Any stills discovered were confiscated. I think the reason it was regarded as a very serious offence was that it was very potent and the effect it had on their behaviour.

I think that cannabis and 'bhang' are one and the same thing, and its consumption would often end in violence. The plant although banned was often found in small plots in river beds or thickets that held a slight shade from an acacia thorn tree. The plant was about three feet tall and grew as a bush, and the leaves at the end of the stalks were as a star about five or six in all, torpedo shaped and about three inches by half an inch. The edges of the leaves were serrated and dark green in colour.

I don't know whether the leaf was chewed or smoked but I suppose the results were the same. It didn't appear to be a serious matter as only very occasionally did I find a person who behaved as though under the influence of the drug. Needless to say when a plot was found and destroyed it could not be established who the perpetrator was.

Roads

If they can be described as such, were terrible in the early years of my life in Kenya. There were only two roads with a tar macadam surface. One was one hundred miles long between Nakuru and Nairobi and built by Italian prisoners of war during the Second World War, and another of about twenty miles from Macinnon Road to Mombasa. I think the latter was surfaced with tar macadam because of the military base there.

All the other roads were just sufficient for two vehicles to pass and about two or three feet below ground with a ditch either side and cut off drains. They were surfaced by a kind of gravel called 'murram' which was freely available near most roads.

During the rainy season it was advisable to try to get to your destination before three o'clock when most of the rain began to fall, and always carry mud chains and a small spade. With luck the mud chains could keep the car moving unless the mud was sticky when it would bung up in the mudguards, which was difficult to clear with a small spade.

The dry season also caused problems. One was the dust, whereby it was too risky to overtake on the narrow road and another was corrugation.

Some said that this corrugation (that is the loose surface) only occurs on or about the Equator had peaks and troughs varying in their distance between peaks and the depths. Some were so bad that it was difficult to drive slowly, whereby the wheels would go into the bottom of the trough, then one would try to get up enough speed so that the wheels rode on the peaks. This could often be done at fifty miles an hour, others with peaks further apart needed sixty or more miles an hour. Only certain makes of cars could take this punishment that the suspension had to withstand.

Later the roads were much improved by raising and widening the road so that it was above ground level and the water could drain on to the adjacent land, and being more exposed to the sun and wind, dried out more quickly. The surface was still made with murram with the exception of main roads which were tar macadam.

The roads on the farm were made by ploughing to the centre and the use of a grader, levelled and shaped but only during the rainy season when the soil could be compacted. Only a few main roads on the farm were surfaced with murram.

Shooting

We had several dams that attracted the migratory ducks and geese, and there were several species of each. On the small dams they could be made to fly over the awaiting guns, and on the bigger ones a home made boat was used to make the ones in the middle fly off. The evening flight was best when shooting alone.

Large flocks of guinea were on the farm and they were driven off the fields of maize by beaters towards the guns that were positioned on the edge of an adjoining wood. These shoots would be in the months of December, January and February whilst the maize was being harvested and the shoot could be done with many good bags.

On a neighbouring farm there was an area of boggy land that was covered in tall grass that concealed quite a number of different species of deer which would feed on the crops nearby. A shoot was organised whereby the deer were driven to awaiting guns that were loaded with buck shot. A few were shot but I considered this method far too dangerous for the participants and declined any further invitations.

I think that the rifle used on a standing target is a better and much safer method of reducing the deer population to an acceptable level.

The Ground Nut Scheme

During the years I was farming in Kenya the groundnut fiasco was begun and ended in neighbouring Tanganyika. By the way the name is derived from the Swahili word 'tanganya' interpreted to mean to "mix ingredients". As the country has many different tribes, altitudes, climates and soils the word is very appropriate, and I think the name was given by the Germans who first colonised the country.

I have an Official Report on the Scheme which is devastating, but there were many more things we heard about which are not in the report.

It was doomed from the start through only having two or three of the directors of the huge operation with any experience of tropical agriculture and the others were ex-servicemen who had neither experience of dealing with a large African labour force or agricultural machinery.

It is unbelievable that the clearing of the bush was done mechanically and very badly, when adequate labour was available to do it effectively and properly supervised.

The mechanised clearing that was done by dragging an anchor chain between two vehicles if it was done when the ground was wet, most of the scrub would be pulled out by the roots, but in dry weather it would break off leaving the roots behind.

We heard from a reliable source that cement was used mistakenly for fertiliser, and the concrete wasn't very good made of fertiliser.

The giant baobab trees that were left after the clearing of the bush were regarded as unsightly and were removed at considerable expense as many were over ten feet in diameter and were bulldozed into rows with the object of burning them. Local knowledge would have told them that they will not burn no matter how long they are left.

A schedule for the maintenance of tractors etc. did not exist and punctured tyres on tractors were ruined driving back to depots.

A modern sawmill was built at a place some fifty miles from the nearest forest. A harbour and docks and pipe lines and a railway were built and never used, and one of the main sites was built between two ranges of hills that caused a gale to blow most of the time and it was also subject to flooding.

When they realised the scheme was a failure and thirty million pounds had gone down the drain, they tried to grow maize for which I sold them a fair quantity of seed. If they had asked I could have told them that the type I grew was useless for that area which was at a low altitude with a limited rainfall and poor soil fertility.

Later I sold them about twenty young boran bulls to diversify into ranching, but it was in the tsetse fly area, and I doubt whether that would be a success either.

I think the only crop that could have had a reasonable chance of success would have been sunflower, and it would have produced the vegetable oil that the scheme was intended to produce.

Given the vast acreage of the scheme it would have had to be harvested mechanically and as the three main varieties that I grew ripened unevenly and were up to ten feet tall, mechanical harvesting could not have been succesful.They would have had to have grown a variety such as grown in America to achieve good results.

A Day's Work

My day would begin at dawn at 6.15 a.m (dawn was at the same time throughout the year). with a cup of tea brought by the house servant, and at 6.30 I would consult with the Headman the work for the day. Perhaps heavy rain the previous day would mean a late start with the tractors for cultivation or planting. All the other headmen and foremen would report at about the same time and they were given instructions and allocated labourers for their specific jobs. The farm clerk would be on hand to take note of where the work was being done and and afterwards he would visit each site and check the identities and numbers on the site.

The storeman would issue tools and make a list. He would also issue fuel for the tractors also oils and greases and allocate them to each machine, and was also responsible to ensure that the oil changes and maintenance schedules were carried out according to that particular tractor.

The Headman of cattle would report any births, deaths or illnesses that had occurred and the state of the grazing.

At 7 o'clock all of the labour would have dispersed to their various jobs and I would then ride one pony to as many sites as possible to inspect the work until breakfast time at 9 a.m.

After breakfast and depending on the type of work to be supervised, and the distance away from the farmstead (the farm was six miles long) I would take the other pony or a car. The pony was better to supervise most of the labour gangs as one was independent of roads and I could cross from one field to another and the labour never knew where I was.

When the combine harvester was at work and certain other work being done by the tractors, I usually took the car, as I found that some of the labour would not hold the pony whilst I made adjustments to the machines, and if I had to return to the homestead to repair something, or get a new part, it took much longer and often the part couldn't be carried on the pony.

Whether by car or pony and often both I continued to supervise work unti 1 p.m. when I had lunch, and again from 3 p.m. until about 5 p.m. I usually went by car to have another look at the tractors or combine that would work until 6.30 when it went dark.

To keep track of all that was being done it was a must that I made a record of everything in my diary as a full report was made out at the end of each month. This was done in the evening when my Headman could come to the office and report things that I may have overlooked and discuss the work to be done the following day, and also work that would be done maybe a week or more ahead.

For instance I had to be sure that all the tools that were needed for a particular work were available and in good order with good shafts made by the carpenter and sharpened and welded by the blacksmith.

As there was no television and the radio programmes were poor and mainly directed at the African, we usually invited friends for a sundowner and dinner once a week, and the hospitality was returned each week.

There was a European Club about six miles away where I played snooker and billiards once a week and on Sundays most of the farmers and their families would spend most of the day there in the swimming pool and have lunch there. On most Sundays we would have a film show when small children would be put to bed in cars parked nearby with a watchman on duty to report to parents if a child was awake or crying. Very seldom did they require assistance as they had had a hectic day in the pool and playing with friends, also the altitude of 6500 feet made them more tired than at sea level.

Pit Sawing

A tribe called Kissii were regarded as experts in digging wells and deep holes for lavatories and also pit sawing. When the shortage of thatching grass forced us to abandon the building of traditional thatched huts here there and everywhere, we built several lines of two roomed houses in brick. Now that the labour was more concentrated, toilets were very important. We found that the minimum size to dig a deep hole was four feet and as it wasn't essential to dig a round one it could be done two feet wide, thereby only two thirds of the soil needed to be excavated. Twenty feet was regarded as the minimum depth whereby no flies would get to the excrement. A concrete slab was placed over the hole with two holes in it, so that it was a double toilet with doors opening in opposite sides. Several of these toilets were dug, where or as required by the labour.

All the timber that was needed on the farm was cut by that tribe of pit sawyers who always had their own saw. They would fell the selected trees, usually found in a river bed and it would be hauled to a site they had prepared for the sawing. After much turning of the log on a gantry that they had made, one side would be cut off in a line that was made by a piece of string rubbed in charcoal, held tight at both ends and plucked to leave a black line. The log was then turned and the cut side placed level on the top. All the different sizes of timber that was to be sawn was marked off by the string, always making an allowance for the width of the saw cut and for shrinkage.

Water Divining and Digging Wells

There were quite a number of springs and streams that were permanent, but down in the valley was not the best place to site a house and farmstead, and if rising ground was only a short distance away a water pump and storage tank could achieve a water supply with minimum expense. But if the distance was say a mile away, and the cost of piping would be high, an alternative was a well.

This was the case on one farm when the services of a water diviner was engaged. He cut a twig that had a fork of equal size about three eighths thick and eighteen inches long. He walked around the site where it was hoped to find water and to our astonishment he found an underground stream which he estimated to be 65 feet down. Afterwards I found that this mysterious feat was available to me.

When water is detected an effort should be made with divining twig to discover whether it is a sump or an underground stream. When a stream is discovered it gives an opportunity to dig a well at a suitable place, but if it is a sump there is no alternative to dig elsewhere.

The depth of the underground water is predicted by divining away from the strongest pull of the twig to where it ceases, and checking by going towards the predicted place to discover where the twig begins to react. This distance is the depth of the underground water.

No time was lost to dig the well four feet in diameter and at fifty feet we dug into water bearing sand that was liable to collapse. Up to that depth the soil was very stable, somewhat like gravel.

WATER DIVINING TWIG

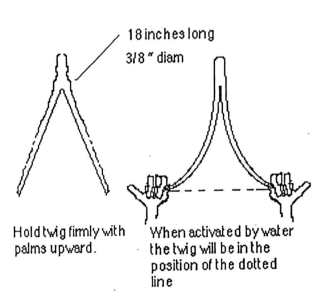

18 inches long
3/8 " diam

Hold twig firmly with palms upward.

When activated by water the twig will be in the position of the dotted line

As some means would have to be made fasten a pump and also to prevent the collapse of the wall of the well, I made a concrete ring that had a spiral top on which spiral brickwork could be built. It was lowered down the well and and the spiral brick work built on to it until well above the unstable water bearing sand. It was then dug deeper and at the depth the water diviner had predicted it could not be dug any further because of the water entering. The water rose about eight feet and was a good supply and clean.

Later another was dug which I predicted would be about fifty six feet deep. Owing to the danger of the well wall collapsing when reaching water bearing soil, it was decided that a prefabricated ring would be used when the well was commenced. The brickwork was done on the surface as it slipped down the well, taking care that the diameter of the spiral brickwork did not increase. At 48 feet it hit an underground stream that came in on one side and out the other. My prediction of the underground stream was correct, but the depth was wrong.

Afterwards I remembered that I had not wet my hands when estimating the depth, perhaps that could have been the reason for the error.

CONCRETE REINFORCED RING (SHOE) FOR BASE OF WELL

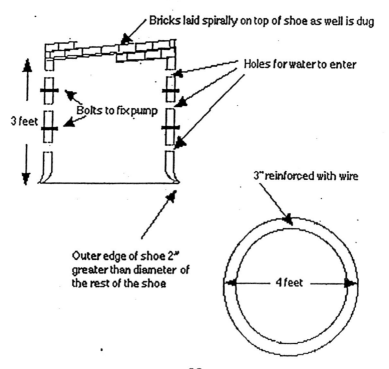

Bricks laid spirally on top of shoe as well is dug

Holes for water to enter

Bolts to fix pump

3 feet

3" reinforced with wire

Outer edge of shoe 2" greater than diameter of the rest of the shoe

4 feet

Grass Fires

In the late 1940s when I arrived in the Trans Nzoia district there were a lot of vacant farms, and the few that were occupied had a limited area of cultivation, whereby there were large areas of indigenous African oat grass that were some 4 feet tall and were a nightmare should fire break out during the dry season. I saw them burn for weeks and extend to 40 miles, they would die down at night, flare up during the day and cross roads and streams.

To protect crops and grazing it was a must to make fire breaks. That was an area 30 feet wide of ploughed land devoid of vegetation. Usually there was cooperation with a neighbour with this task if there was one.

Many times we have had fires break out within the farm when an alarm bell was rung and all the workers had to turn out to extinguish it. Often the fires were so fierce that one couldn't get near to beat them out, then the only way was to burn back. This was done by finding a footpath or an area of shorter grass some distance ahead of the fire, and light a line of fire, making sure to extinguish the grass fire on the side away from the main fire. Even if there was a wind blowing it was found that there was little or no wind ahead of the main fire, it created a kind of vacuum.

It was customary to give all the workers who had turned out to fight the fire, a day's pay, but once we had several fires and my Headman told me these fires were no accident, and had been started deliberately to get a day's pay. So no day's pay was given, the fires stopped.

I remember once during the 1950s that the whole district was covered in smoke for weeks on end and it was believed that the papyrus on the Nile in Sudan was on fire. It must have been a big fire as the site was 400 miles away.

The Kang Gilli (bell)

This was a plough disc that was worn away to be no longer useful and hung on a wire near the office and store, and when hit hard with a piece of metal the sound could be heard four or five miles away (as there were no other sounds of motorways etc. to compete with it.)

As very few workers had a watch or clock and didn't know the time except when the sun shone, a long ring of the bell was the time to start work, a short one would denote that rations were being issued, and a different one was to denote that wages were

69

due to be paid.

A smaller disc that was cracked was used by the school master to call his pupils.

I mentioned the time that the sun shone. It is because the time can be determined to within about ten minutes by the shadow of the sun as we were only one degree north of the Equator. The sun was directly overhead in March and September at one o'clock, and slightly to the south in June, and to the north in December.The length of the east to west shadow gave the hours of the day, which remained almost the same throughout the year and with a minimum of practice the time could be estimated.

Rabies

This terrible disease was rife throughout Kenya and action was taken by the Veterinary Dept. in 1956 to try to eradicate it.

First of all it was decided with the agreement of the headmen that the number of dogs kept by labour should be reduced to a minimum, and that only employees that had the need for a dog to assist with their duties should be permitted to keep one. Thereby only Ascaris (policemen), herdsmen and those engaged in protection of crops and stores were given written permission with a description of the dog.

Only a few brought their dogs to be destroyed at a date that it was decided it was to be carried out, and that it was a matter of hunting down the rest of them. I was somewhat apprehensive on hunting them down. Should I delegate an employee to do this unpleasant task or should I do it myself? I decided it was my responsibility.

I shot several without protest, and then the women folk thought it a good idea to stop them disturbing their sleep with all the noise they made, and became very enthusiastic spotters for the remaining dogs that I had missed, and in all I shot about twenty.

The dogs that were authorised together with my two dogs were given an injection by the Vet. Dept. with a certificate, and they were repeated at six month intervals. Maybe you are aware of this dreadful disease which I believe is incurable unless injections are given as soon as possible after a bite by a rabid dog. It involves 14 injections at two day intervals into the flesh of the stomach wall. If one is not carrying much flesh I believe it is a very painful ordeal. I think it was just before the eradication scheme that one morning I was confronted by one of my dogs, a bull terrier, that bared its teeth and the hairs on its back stood on end, instead of the

70

usual greeting and tail wagging. I lost no time getting my gun and shot it.

The carcase was sent to the Vet. Dept. for a post mortem , but it was not confirmed that it had rabies, but I felt sure that it had had been better to have been safe than sorry.

Civil Uprisings and Strikes

Dealing with the latter first. They did not exist as far as I was concerned. Many times there were threats of strikes but as I ensured that my labour force was divided equally between three tribes who could not agree amongst themselves, they petered out. When they were told that if they did not like my instructions that were necessary for running the farm, or that were for the benefit of our community, they would be paid any wages outstanding and could leave the farm and try to find employment elsewhere, where they may find rules and regulations were more to their liking.

There was one uprising by the Kitosh tribe that centred on the town of Mumias in the year (I think) 1948, that a punitive force of the Kenya African Rifles was sent to quell. Members of the tribe said that a number of their tribe were killed, but as nothing was reported in the newspapers it could not be confirmed, but it was noted that the particular tribe were rather more subdued in their behaviour.

The Mau Mau uprising in the 1950s was on a bigger scale and very violent. The Kikuyu tribe were responsible for this and members of the tribe were forced to take an oath against Europeans and Government or be mutilated or killed if they refused.

According to the Official Report it was two or three years before the seriousness of the situation as reported by the District Officers was acted upon by the Government. I believe the uprising was about to spread into the Wakamba tribe when action was taken because that tribe were predominantly recruited into the Police and the Army.

That some difficulty was experienced in controlling it was the fact that this community was scattered over a wide area with just a few houses here and there. The solution was to contain them in wired compounds where a degree of control could be exercised over most of them, and the hardliners then formed themselves into gangs that operated from the forests.

There were many atrocities on the Europeans as well as

71

members of their own tribe who refused to take the oath. The mutilations that were inflicted and reported were too horrible to describe and a friend of mine who was killed outright could have considered himself lucky not to have endured the torture and prolonged death of others.

He was called out late one night on the pretence of something to do with the cattle on the farm. He always wore a cardigan with wide sleeves into which he tucked his hands and always walked with his head down. As he walked past a tree on the lawn his head was severed from his body with one stroke of a panga and so quickly that his hands were still in the sleeves of his cardigan.

There were three incidents on the farm. One was that the Kikuyu that I employed to grow vegetables for the labour were suspected of being Mau Mau and I was very strongly advised by my Headman that they should be removed immediately, as they were using very 'bad language'. When questioned about the matter he did not say that murder was spoken of, but was emphatic that they be removed without delay.

I reported to the Labour Officer who was involved with security, and he did not want to remove them from the farm, but when asked why he would not give a reason, but he admitted he would have to agree to my request.

They were removed and their houses burnt down. Later I found out that they were supposed to be acting as informers, but in reality they were hard core Mau Mau and had deceived the Labour Officer.

Another incident was that I had three cows hamstrung, that is, the tendons above the hock were slashed and they were unable to stand on their hind feet. It was a terrible sight to see them struggling to get up. I shot them to put them out of their misery.

As this happened near to the houses of three Kikuyu I employed, I asked them for an explanation of the incident and said if they would not divulge who was responsible they would be removed forthwith. They were too frightened to divulge anything. I was very sorry to see them go as two of them were very good at pruning coffee trees and the other was an excellent carpenter.

During the Mau Mau uprising I was a member of the Special Police, and our duties were mainly to assist the Army in carrying out raids on various farms. The usual procedure was that the Army would place a cordon round the selected group of farms at night fall and a few hours later we would enter all the houses and interrogate the occupants and establish their identities. Any suspects were removed and taken away by the Army for further interrogation. As none of the Army could speak their languages or knew their customs I think we played an important role in these raids.

During this time I remember a remarkable incident when a large group of Kikuyu men were assembled in the local Police Station, and all were lined up before a Witch Doctor. I think there was a kind of bower they had to pass through, and the Doctor held something in his hand that looked like entrails, which were passed around the head of each and I think also touched their lips.

This was accompanied by a lot of Mumbo Jumbo that I could not understand. It was a de-oathing ceremony. The Security Forces must have been desperate to solve this uprising when they had to resort to a practice that was previously banned.

There was also a scheme whereby groups of European families were to be gathered together in some of the bigger houses which had a clear view around them and two roads of access. It didn't take place because the security situation improved.

Su - Ku - Koo. (Christmas)
I do not know the origin of the word or from what language it is, the Swahili word for God is Mungu; however they joined us in the celebration of this occasion with gusto.

There was a two day holiday with pay and a fairly big ox was slaughtered and I personally handed it out in proportion to the size of the family of the labourer. I considered it unfair to give the bachelors the same as the family man who might have two wives and a lot of children. Permission was given for all who wanted to, to brew beer, and a few who were short of maize meal for the brew were given extra.

The school children were each given a packet of sweets and it was stressed that our custom of giving presents was that it should be reciprocated. I was surprised at the extent that this custom was taken by them as very few of them were Christians. So I kept a stock of sweets, tobacco, and other things to exchange for the gifts they brought such as eggs, fowls, vegetables and fruits etc.

On the afternoon of Christmas Day a group of women and girls dressed in their very best, and carrying some greenery such as banana leaves would come to our house singing and form a circle on the lawn. A cheer leader would be in the centre and dance about

73

while singing and the others would join in a chorus, waving their greenery and also dancing about. I could not determine the odd words that were spoken, I think they were of the tribal language. The performance would last about half an hour and all of them were given a present.

Karamojong

This tribe inhabit the north west area of Kenya known as Karamoja, it is a large area of semi-desert, sparsely inhabited and with very few roads or tracks of access.

They are Nilotic and pastoral, similar to the Masai, Nandi, and Suk, wear a minimum of clothing, and their manner may be described as haughty and they consider themselves to be superior to the Bantu tribes.

Once during a busy season when I was rather short of labour, I employed three of this tribe as guards to crops and stores. I understood that they went around the labour lines and warned the occupants that they had been given orders to protect certain crops and stores, and warned them that they would be dealt with severely if they were caught stealing. This warning was taken seriously as the other tribes were terrified of them, and needless to say nothing was stolen.

Later, six or seven more of that tribe asked for work and I engaged them and gave them some old sacks that they could stuff with grass or straw to make a mattress. My storeman asked why I had given them the sacks and I told him that it would make them more comfortable at night and that I was sure that he himself had some sort of mattress and why shouldn't they have one.

He said that these persons were not human, they were animals and that they would never have had a building to sleep in never mind a mattress. They slept out in the open under trees and the sacks I had given them would be used as fuel for cooking, as it was a custom of that tribe that the work of collecting and cutting fuel was womens' work.

I was warned by an old farmer settler that it was unwise to have so many of that tribe, and it was advisable to keep the numbers down to three or four. This warning proved correct as they would not take orders from my headman and caused trouble in the labour lines and within a week I had to get rid of them.

On a neighbouring farm there were quite a number of them near a road that led to a large sisal estate, and it was reported that several of the employees of that estate went missing. It was later

74

that several bodies were found naked and partly hidden, and it was rumoured that they had been killed for the use of their clothing for fuel. I think they were exaggerating, it could have been for their possessions, but why had they been stripped naked?

Conclusion

When the history of Kenya is written, the years 1946 to§ 1962 will I am sure be recorded as the most momentous of all.

Transportation was improved beyond belief, in that from having only a short flying strip for small aircraft, it developed an international air terminal capable of accommodating the largest aircraft with facilities to match, and an improved network of internal airports.

From only having one hundred and fifty miles of tar-macadamed roads in this fairly large country to a completed network of modern highways connecting all major towns from Kitale in the north to Mombasa at the coast, that enabled residents and transportation vehicles to travel by day or night, instead of being bogged down in mud every afternoon during the rainy seasons. Mini coaches were able to operate frequently between most towns.

The railway network was not extended, but improved timetables, and I think more rolling stock were acquired and were adequate for the volume of traffic that had multiplied. I never experienced any shortage of rolling stock to convey maize, wheat, barley, sunflower, live cattle or pigs to their ultimate destination.

The maize crop increased by the way of better husbandry and improved seed, whereby the needs of Tanganyika and Uganda were supplied over and above the local requirements and a surplus was exported of good quality to corn-flake manufacturers and brewers.

I don't think any wheat or barley was exported other than to Tanganyika and Uganda.

There did not appear to be any increase in the acreage of coffee on European owned estates, but in the African locations of Kiambu and the Mount Kenya areas there was quite an increase. The Coffee Board appeared to be efficient in maintaining the high quality of the product that was mainly used in blending.

The production of tea was increased many times by plantations in Tinderet, Mumias and on the Cherangani foothills, that was over and above that of the existing estates at Kericho.

The bacon factory at Uplands always seemed short of their requirements, and I believe that many of their products were exported.

The market for pyrethrum seemed to have been maintained despite the fact that many chemicals had been discovered that would replace it much cheaper. It could be said that the environmental organisations were influencing some people to the view that natural products were more friendly. As far as I am aware there was no increase in the acreage of the plant during those years.

The sisal plantations were almost wiped out by the invention of polypropylene twine. In the early years a large acreage was grown in the low rainfall areas that was made into binder twine and other articles.

The Livestock Commission with its slaughterhouses at the Athi River and Mombasa did a good job of dealing with the number of livestock in the African locations that were becoming seriously overstocked. I am not sure whether any prime beef was exportedbut I believe that surplus stock from the African locations was made into corned beef and exported.

The Cooperative Creameries opened more depots and would take all the cream farmers could produce.. I think most of it was made into butter and exported to the Near East markets.

Opportunities existed for rogue graders to exploit grading of maize wheat and cream by false readings of moisture and foreign matter content in the former and declaring that the cream was sour, and expecting 'backhanders'. On the very few occasions this was firmly dealt with by the management but I could see this could become a problem if management and supervision became lax.

During the first few years there was a rather peculiar practice (or should I say custom) that local traders were very good indeed with their credit facilities in that they allowed a year of credit. It was no surprise when this ceased and monthly credit became the normal. I wondered if this facility could have survived from the custom in England years before when the nobility settled their accounts half yearly or more!

It was a paradise as far as law and order was concerned, Small items that were left lying around were sometimes stolen but muggings, car theft and hijacking were unheard of.

Having seen the African develop from walking to riding a

bicycle and to driving a car, and from being clad in skins to wearing suits it was quite a transformation over a few years.

Tourism or safaris (Swahili for 'journey') did not exist in the early years except for the safaris of big game hunters to shoot fine specimens in a country teeming with big game. The most important development of the tourist industry was the air transport whereby it took only a few hours as against weeks travel by boat. No doubt advertising and conservation also played a part..

Independence was gained by the country during my time and as I was in an area of the country dominated by the Kitosh, Jalua, Bugishu and Nandi tribes there was no enthusiasm at all for the transfer of political power by the labour force. They appeared contented with the progress that had been made, and pleaded with me to stay as they did not trust a future African government dominated by the Kikuyu tribe to look after their welfare, or that justice would be upheld, and feared corruption.

There was little industrial development and I believe that the success achieved was by agriculture, with expertise and management and dedication of grass roots farmers from the British Isles who immigrated during that period.

Surengu (the author)

The author was born in 1919 on a small tenanted mixed upland farm in the Pennines, the eldest of 3 brothers and 3 sisters.

He was educated at local school until fourteen, and then worked on the farm, producer-retailing milk and eggs and tending sheep and cattle on a moor stray.

Called up for war service in early 1941 into the R.A.F. Provost Corps, he served in India from mid 1942 to the end of 1945 with the rank of Sergeant, and was demobbed in 1946.

He married in 1948 and has a family of one daughter and four sons.

He farmed in Kenya first as manager and then on his own account from 1948 to 1962.

From 1962 he farmed a mixed farm in Yorkshire. During that time he served on several N.F.U. committees, was Chairman of the Board of Directors for a Farm Supply Company, Chairman of his Parish Council, and Chairman of two Village Hall committees.

He retired in 1982 and took up the hobbies of grandfather clock repairing, deep sea fishing, growing prize gooseberries and beekeeping.